It Takes More Than Guts

Phillip Van Hooser

It Takes More Than Guts

Life-changing discoveries about surviving and
overcoming IBD and chronic illness

By Phillip Van Hooser

Phillip Van Hooser, MBA, CSP
Van Hooser Associates, Inc.
Post Office Box 643
Princeton, KY 42445
(270) 365-1536 • (270) 365-6678
phil@vanhooser.com
www.ItTakesMoreThanGuts.com

Editor
Al Borowski, Med, CSP
Priority Communication Skills, Inc.
Pittsburgh, Pennsylvania

Cover Design
Pam Moore
Moore Designs
Brentwood, Tennessee

Cover Photos
Danny Beavers
Princeton, Kentucky

Library of Congress Catalog Control Number: 2003096152

ISBN: 1-893322-23-8

Printed in the United States of America

Perspectives on *It Takes More Than Guts*

"*It Takes More Than Guts* is the wonderful story of one man's journey with ulcerative colitis. With rare sensitivity, Phillip Van Hooser shares his and his family's moving experience as they struggle to cope with his disease. To individuals and families who know the awful toll imposed by chronic illness, his story will resonate with truth and valuable information. For others, it will provide a poignant insight into the enormous, everyday achievements of people who live in the horrific shadow of chronic illness. We applaud Phillip Van Hooser for bringing to publication this excellent and much needed book."

Shelby and William D. Modell
National Co-Founders
Crohn's & Colitis Foundation of America

"This very personal autobiography written by Phillip Van Hooser reveals the unspoken realities of living with Inflammatory Bowel Disease and chronic illness with candor, compassion and a healthy sense of humor. In this survivor's guide, patients will find a sympathetic friend and receive great encouragement from someone who has been there."

Rolf Benirschke
Former San Diego Charger Kicker
Author of *Alive & Kicking* and
Great Comebacks from Ostomy Surgery

"Gray's Anatomy taught us about guts—so does Phillip Van Hooser. In *It Takes More Than Guts*, Mr. Van Hooser takes us along in his valiant battle to save his colon—and his life. His insights into what goes on on the other end of our stethoscopes are a 'must-read' for all health care professionals in the bowels of medicine."

Patricia L. Raymond MD
Gastroenterology Consultants LTD
Author of *Don't Jettison Medicine: Resuscitate*
Your Passion for the Career You Loved

"*It Takes More Than Guts* paints a picture that *ordinary* people put behind the eight ball can do *extraordinary* things. It's amazing what we can do when tested. Remember, *we all* will be tested at one time or another in our lives. Are you ready? *It Takes More Than Guts* is a 101 course in learning that valuable lesson."

Peter Nielsen
Former Mr. International Universe, Author and Host of Syndicated TV and Radio Show *Peter's Principles*

"It was fascinating to see the view from the other side of the examination room table."

Richard Truesdale MD
Gastroenterology Associates of Ocala

"I wish this book had been available when I was first diagnosed with Crohn's disease! What a difference it would have made in my life. I felt so alone and even my doctors had no idea what to do. They told me I did it to myself with stress because of my show business career. This book is important for all who suffer and all who love them."

Mary Ann Mobley
Actress & Former Miss America

"Do not miss this book. Whether you suffer from ulcerative colitis, another chronic illness or have ever been faced with a difficult obstacle in your life, Phillip Van Hooser's insight and storytelling will play a major role in your comeback."

Chris Gedney
Former Arizona Cardinals Tight End

"Everyone, at various points in their life, will face challenges. This book is about a very serious and unforeseen challenge and how that challenge was met. Gritty and medically accurate, *It Takes More Than Guts* is not just about a disease and a complicated medical procedure. Phillip Van Hooser speaks with deep emotion and easy humor about how he faced his particular challenge and, along the way, invites all of us to meet our own personal challenges with grace and style. Sufferers and friends of sufferers of IBD will find the book useful for its accuracy and empathy. I highly recommend this book!"

Martin Ramsay
President, CEATH Company

Table of Contents

Dedication

This book is dedicated to the men and women,
boys and girls around the world
who struggle with the realities of IBD every day.

May this book encourage and sustain
you and those who support you.

Acknowledgements

This is a book that I didn't *want* to write. However, over time I determined this is a book I *needed* to write. Though I crafted the words that make up this book and committed them to paper, there were dozens of others who helped in their own way to make this book available to you. I want to take this opportunity to thank them publicly.

I begin by thanking all those hundreds of individuals who served as a constant source of encouragement to me as I battled for two years to save my colon from the ravages of ulcerative colitis. Though I eventually surrendered my diseased colon to the surgeon's knife, the thoughts, prayers, words, cards, hugs, pats and smiles I received from so many wonderful people lifted my spirits in ways they will never know. I especially want to recognize the membership of the First Baptist Church, Ocala, Florida and specifically, my Sunday School class for their relentless support. Though we are separated now, I will never forget you.

I owe a tremendous debt of gratitude to my dear friends Joe and Karen Owen who made their house on Kentucky Lake available to me for more than ten months as I pushed to finish the writing of "*Guts.*" They believed in me and I appreciate them.

I consulted with a number of medical professionals during the writing of this book to ensure the accuracy of the content. Each added a unique perspective and therefore made the final effort that much better. Thanks are well deserved and go out to Drs. Michael Fisher, Brian Guthrie, Glen Morgan, Patricia Raymond and Richard Truesdale. Additionally, I wish to thank Carol Shrum and Carla Zimmerman.

I have been blessed to have a number of people who were willing to read chapter after chapter and offer their honest feedback. Each holds a special place in my heart. They are Dr. Buddy Cocke, Chris Gedney, Susan Friedmann, Brad and Cindy Fleetwood, Tom and Carrie Alexander, Patrick Donadio, Rolf Benirschke, Gavin Lindberg,

Rodger DeRose, Mary Ann Mobley-Collins, John Paling, Laura Fagin, Marilynn Mobley, Gregg Treadway, Bob Layne, Greg Hyland and Jeff Tobe.

Extra credit goes to four very special proofreaders. Jean Gatz, the "Comma Queen;" Kim Mercer, "N-9;" Pat Miksch, my high school grammar teacher; and Martin Ramsay, the "Borborygmus Kid." Thank you all for the dozens of hours you dedicated to this project. I don't know how I could have done it without you.

The man who edited my first book and now my second was Al Borowski. Al is not only a pro, he is an encourager. That's a wonderful combination.

To my family and my friends that might as well be family—Kerry "Crow" Crawford, Marc and Kim Mercer, Ed Johnson, John Alvarez, Anthony Stallins, Jim McDaniel, Anna Jo Wyman, Patti Blackburn, Mom and Bob, Merlin and Pat, Ellen, Mark and Dan. You will never know how much having you standing beside me meant.

To my children Joe, Sarah and Sophie, you made me want to get better.

Finally, to my wife, Susan. You exemplified what grace under pressure looks like. The courage that sustained me, I drew from you. I love you.

Foreword

I did not realize when I asked Phillip Van Hooser to speak at an employee communication meeting back in 1994 that it would be the beginning of an enriching professional and personal relationship. I was working for the firm Arthur Andersen then, and I was so impressed with Phil's message of motivational leadership that I invited him back to present at these meetings several more times.

After I retired from Arthur Andersen, I stayed in touch with Phil. It was then I learned about his crippling battle with ulcerative colitis and I made it a point to keep in touch throughout his long process of recovery.

Ulcerative colitis and Crohn's disease are collectively known as inflammatory bowel diseases, or IBD. These diseases cause severe inflammation in the intestines, which can lead to debilitating symptoms and a sense of isolation for people who suffer from IBD.

As fate would have it, in March of 2002, I agreed to join the Crohn's and Colitis Foundation of America (CCFA) as President and Chief Executive Officer. I wanted to help advance the effort to find a cure for Crohn's disease and ulcerative colitis. These diseases affect up to one million Americans, including several people in my own family. Yet, often it is only when we reveal our connection to CCFA that we find out that someone we know for a long time suffers from the disease. I called Phil to ask how he was doing and to let him know about my new position.

Phil immediately offered to help CCFA in any way he could by volunteering to use his professional skills as a motivational speaker for the foundation. Just name it, he said. I didn't hesitate to take him up on his offer! I was also moved by his generosity. Here he was in the midst of his own recovery, yet thinking about how he could be helpful to others who also had IBD.

Phil's first assignment was to act as an emcee for CCFA's annual meeting, bring his message and motivation to CCFA chapter staff and volunteers from all across the country. The audience connected immediately, as there is instant kinship among those who live with IBD. He was so popular CCFA chapters instantly clamored for him to appear at their galas, and Phil was glad to share his story. Phil was also an important part of CCFA's First National IBD Advocacy Conference in Washington, D.C., where he hosted the award luncheon for Senator Harry Reid. Senator Reid introduced the IBD Act, the first IBD-specific legislation ever introduced in the U.S. Congress. Phil was there to share his personal experience and advocate for passage of the bill by visiting his Kentucky legislators!

Phil has demonstrated a strong commitment to CCFA, and with this book, extends that commitment to helping all those with IBD, their families and friends. There is nothing so liberating for people with Crohn's disease and ulcerative colitis than when someone stands up and tells his story. Phil's inspiring account of his struggle with ulcerative colitis is an open, honest discussion about what it's like to live with IBD.

This moving journal of a patient's view of battling and surviving ulcerative colitis will help patients and professionals better understand the daily burdens of living with this debilitating illness. Through this intensely personal account, Phil is doing what he does best – speaking out and motivating others. He reveals the mental and physical perseverance that it takes to sustain the entire process of living with ulcerative colitis to its ultimate conclusion – surgical removal of the colon. It is motivating to read about such a triumph in the fight against IBD, and this book will be an inspiration to every reader. More importantly, this personal account of living with IBD will let others know they are not alone and that they, too, can triumph over this life-changing illness.

I am grateful that Phil decided to share his story and I applaud him for his leadership in the fight against ulcerative colitis.

Rodger L. DeRose, President and Chief Executive Officer
Crohn's and Colitis Foundation of America

Introduction

WARNING: THIS BOOK MAY NOT BE RIGHT FOR YOU

That sounds like a strange way to introduce a book, doesn't it? It may sound strange, but it's true. This book may not be right for you. It certainly won't be right for everybody. It wasn't intended to be.

What you are holding in your hands is a compelling story—the story of one man's struggle with a serious chronic illness. But this powerful story is also the story of more than one million Americans and millions of other human beings around the world. This story recounts in vivid detail a two-year period in the life of an Inflammatory Bowel Disease (IBD) patient.

Like most stories involving chronic illness, this one begins with the onset of troublesome symptoms and then progresses to the point where the sufferer requires significant medical intervention. That's the foundation of the story. But it is what happens in the "meantime" that makes this story so beneficial to the reader.

As the story unfolds, the author shares valuable information drawn from extensive and comprehensive research into the symptoms, causes, treatment options, medications and diet that any Crohn's disease or ulcerative colitis sufferer can benefit from. But there is more. Much more.

The author also provides an invaluable peek behind the curtain into the mind of a sufferer. This position offers a rare, unique and honest vantage point from which to view the specific emotional and psychological concerns, fears, anxieties and expectations of those who struggle with uncertainty, pain and physical debilitation.

This book is not a warm, fuzzy fairytale where a handsome prince comes sweeping in to rescue the fair maiden just in the nick of time. This book is about real life. This book is about what happens when the handsome prince doesn't make an appearance. This book offers a roadmap as to what needs to be done to survive and thrive in the face of seemingly insurmountable circumstances. Unlike "reality TV" (*Survivor, Who Wants to Be a Millionaire? The Weakest Link)* this is "reality life" on paper, in black and white.

The story you are about to read may be more extreme than the experience of one IBD sufferer and less extreme than another. That is one of the exasperating aspects of this disease. No two cases, no two experiences, are exactly alike. But the experience of one person can serve as a good example of what others might generally expect and prepare for when facing IBD or other chronic illnesses.

Is there pain and suffering detailed here? Yes, there is. It has not been sugarcoated.

Is the book *all* about pain and suffering? No, it's not. Life is not all pain and suffering, even for IBD sufferers. There are marvelous and redeeming examples of humor, friendship, love, hope, restoration and healing found in the following pages.

In addition to providing honest, factual information, the author has tried to make this story, as readable and understandable as possible. With that in mind, as you read the story you will happen upon words and phrases highlighted by ***bold italicized print***. This indicates that the particular word or phrase is described in more detail in the **Just for Understanding…A Glossary of Important Terms** section in the back of the book. The **Glossary** descriptions are intended to replace "medical lingo" with language laypersons can readily understand. Well over one hundred words and phrases are listed and defined in the **Glossary**.

Toward the back of the book, you will find another unique feature. This section is entitled **Just the Facts…About IBD.** Here you will be able to have many of your questions answered quickly and succinctly. What is Inflammatory Bowel Disease? What causes IBD? What are the symptoms of IBD? Who gets IBD? What kinds of diets work for IBD? Other helpful resources are also included with this information.

You will also find a section called **Just Ask Phil...Straight Answers to Difficult Questions**. Many people have practical questions they would love to have answered but are hesitant, for one reason or another, to ask. In this section the author has compiled many of the questions he has been asked privately about his experience. He then shares candid answers that IBD sufferers and their supporters alike will find helpful.

Finally, if you are interested in even more information than this book provides, go to www.ItTakesMoreThanGuts.com or call 270-365-1536 and ask for more information on ***It Takes More Than Guts Caring In Action!*** This special DVD companion piece features on-camera interviews with a broad range of individuals possessing personal knowledge of the challenges of living with, working with and treating those who suffer from IBD. The interviews offer first person insights from doctors, nurses, family members and the patient himself. This unique product allows you to read—and watch—the important story unfold.

There is no other book available that addresses the specific aspects of the challenges facing IBD sufferers as thoroughly as does ***It Takes More Than Guts***.

So, is this book right for you? Is it right for someone you know who needs some straight talk, solid information and personal encouragement? If so, then you will find value in the pages that follow.

1

You Don't Tug On Superman's Cape

4:37 a.m.

From where I lay, I could distinctly read the bold red numbers displayed on the digital clock across the bedroom. For this night, like too many before it, the clock, with its silent numbers unfailingly marking time, served as the physical object of my pent-up frustration.

First, it was 11:23 p.m., then again at 1:16 a.m., a third trip at 2:48 a.m. and now, 4:37 a.m. Hour after frustrating hour, the illuminated numbers constantly reminded me of both the current time and the amount of sleep of which I had once again been deprived. In this sleepless state, fatigue was my only companion. How I longed for sleep and the unconscious escape that only sleep could provide. Desperately, I thought, *Maybe, if I close my eyes tightly and will myself to sleep, I will feel better when I wake.*

But my optimism betrayed me. As I lay desperately longing for relief, once again suffering came calling. Suddenly, as many times before with no preparatory warning, a sharp, gripping pain struck somewhere deep in the hollow of my abdomen. The pain, coupled with fierce cramping, caused me to sit straight up in my bed.

I struggled quickly to my feet. The feeling of ***urgency*** was unmistakable. There was no time for delay. For the fourth time, in the six and one half-hours since I retired for the night, I repeated my blind dash to the bathroom.

Blind because this routine had become so familiar to me in recent weeks that I seldom turned on the light. There was no need. I knew too well where I was headed. I knew too well how I would feel once I got there. Somehow, in its black emptiness, the darkness of our slumbering home offered a slight measure of comfort, temporarily shielding from physical view the helplessness of the pain I was enduring.

By the time I reached the security of the bathroom and had taken my seat yet again, that all too familiar feeling of numbing ***nausea*** had swept over me. Sitting, doubled forward—the physical response to the pain in my cramping gut—I felt the wet drops of perspiration on bare skin as they streamed down my forehead, nose and earlobes, before tumbling down onto my exposed thighs and knees. The sudden intestinal discharge was basically uncontrolled, painful and yet, somehow comforting. Comforting, in that similar past experiences had taught me that a fleeting, temporary period of relief soon followed these repeating episodes of ***diarrhea***.

As I sat, waiting in the darkness for the cramping to subside, I became increasingly more frustrated. Through the confusing haze of exhaustion and nausea, I wondered again and again, *What's happening to me? Why can't I shake this thing?*

Therein lay the frustration. To this point in my life, every significant problem I had ever experienced I had been able to either work through or wait out. That's how I was taught. That's how I was raised. Mental and physical determination, toughness and bravery were highly prized and often stressed personal characteristics in the Van Hooser household during my formative years. Whatever the circumstances we were repeatedly encouraged to stay strong; be tough; keep going; never give in. Over time we had learned our lessons well.

I remember my older sister, Ellen, starting to work as a "check-out girl" at a local grocery store when she was about fifteen years old. Her job required her to be on her feet for extended periods. This perpetual standing, hour after hour after hour on unyielding concrete floors, over time contributed to the development of a troublesome and painful case of varicose veins. So troublesome, in fact, eventually surgery was required to "strip" the affected veins.

As difficult and painful as the procedure was for her, after a brief period of recovery Ellen returned to her checkout responsibilities. She went on to work her way through a private college, demonstrating grit and determination that served her well in her chosen career as a professional educator.

I still remember the pain I saw etched in my sister's face. I also remember family members and friends bragging on my sister, extolling the virtues of her "won't quit" attitude. That impressed me. Even as a young boy, I knew I wanted people to think of me like that.

My younger brother, Mark, was as tough as they come, too. At about age three, Mark bounced off one of those spring-mounted rocking horses that were so popular with young children during the Roy Rogers, *My Friend Flicka* years of the 1950's and 60's. On this occasion, Mark's faithful steed threw him, face first, onto a concrete porch. The force of the fall caused my little brother to bite completely through his bottom lip. The blood and ensuing confusion were terrifying. Stitches were unavoidable.

Upon arriving at the local hospital's emergency room to have the lip stitched back together, the confusion continued. After evaluating the injury, considering the tender age of the young patient and determining the proper medical procedure, the attending doctor and nurses immediately began making plans to physically restrain my little brother. Their tool of choice? The juvenile equivalent of a straight jacket—a sheet in which they intended to wrap and immobilize Mark.

That's when my father intervened. He believed my baby brother was tougher than that. Stepping to Mark's bedside, with nothing more than my father's physical presence and a few simple words of encouragement, Mark, of his own accord, lay perfectly still in anticipation of the procedure.

The doctor stepped forward cautiously, not knowing what to expect, and began administering the necessary injections directly into the affected area to deaden the pain, after which the gaping wound was stitched closed.

All the while, my brother just lay there and took it. As one might imagine, the example of my brother's mental and physical toughness became the stuff of family legend. That heroic toughness was trumpeted at every available occasion. I took note.

I remember yet another occasion that made an impression on me during my early years. Just two or three short years after Mark's rocking horse incident, he once again had need of medical attention. Due to the frequent occurrence and persistence of colds and infections, our family physician determined that the best course of preventative treatment would be to remove Mark's tonsils. Tonsillectomies were a fairly common medical procedure for juvenile patients in the 1960's, and Mark appeared to be a perfect candidate.

While attempting to reassure my parents as to the necessity and relative safety of Marks's pending surgical procedure, family lore holds that the good doctor off-handedly remarked, "This is a very common problem we see in many elementary-aged children. As a matter of fact, sooner or later the chances are very good your other boy there (referring to me), will probably need to have his tonsils removed as well."

My dad, the eternal pragmatist, saw no need to wait. To him, the wisdom—and convenience—of having tonsillectomies for two sons at the same time was obvious. I've since wondered if our dad was able to negotiate a behind the scenes, "two-for-the-price-of-one," "this week only" surgical deal. I'm convinced he at least considered the possibility. In any event, both surgeries took place.

A couple of days after the surgery, Mark had made a remarkable recovery. His ***incision*** was healing well, while his appetite and energy had returned. I on the other hand, was still struggling.

My throat was so sore and swollen that not only was I not eating all the delicious ice cream I had been promised, I had not eaten a bite of anything for almost three days. Time was quickly approaching for us to be released from the hospital, but the nurses explained that the doctor would not sign our release forms until I had successfully taken nourishment by mouth.

There was only one problem—I had absolutely no interest in eating. And I continued to be uninterested until one especially surly pediatric nurse explained, in rather graphic detail, the fine art of intravenous feeding. The idea of another needle held absolutely no appeal for me. I quickly got the picture.

I'm a little embarrassed to admit that possibly my first act of recorded bravery came about thirty minutes later when I swallowed a half dozen or so bites of Campbell's Chicken Noodle soup. Considering how raw and sore my throat was at the time, I was certain I was swallowing that chicken's feet, beak and feathers along with its noodles!

Nevertheless, this highly heralded act of bravery (at least as communicated by my loving parents and several impatient nurses) had its reward. It earned us our freedom. We were soon sprung from the restrictive confines of our sterile prison/hospital room and the overbearing attention inflicted upon us by our guards/nurses.

I realize that these and other early childhood experiences and the foundational attitudes they fostered were of immense help as I struggled through night after sleepless night of cramps, fever and diarrhea. My resolve, though frequently tested, had been cemented years before. The older I get, the more convinced I become that we are the sum total of our previous life experiences. Our choices and actions in the "here and now" are in large part dependent on what we learned "there and then."

My conscious thoughts were not fixed on the memories of varicose veins, spring-loaded rocking horses and tonsillectomies as I sat straddling that porcelain throne in the early morning darkness. But those lessons of strength and resilience, learned long ago, were in some unconscious way still supporting me. The determination, toughness and even bravery that were encouraged, cheered and rewarded earlier in my life was exactly what I thought I needed now to sustain me.

However the ordeal was just beginning. I could never have imagined how much more trying this ordeal would become in the days, weeks and months ahead. Would my determination, toughness and courage be enough?

To this point, as a forty-one-year-old man I had enjoyed good health all my life. Even during those brief, temporary episodes of seasonal colds or the flu du jour I labored on gamely. That's what real men did. I was sure it was. When a man becomes a man—marries, has children, takes on professional responsibility—he simply doesn't let little personal inconveniences, like not feeling good, stand in the way of doing those things that need to be done. I watched my father and mother live their lives that way. Apparently, I was a good student. I had watched carefully and learned well. Now the time had come for me to be Superman, too.

Since leaving the hallowed halls of higher education two decades earlier I had become a husband, father, entrepreneur, business owner and employer. Along the way, I acquired real-world responsibilities and the real-world headaches that often accompany them. I didn't worry though. When things got tough, my resolve simply strengthened. I would step into that imaginary phone booth in my mind and emerge—Super Phil! Faster than a speeding deadline; more powerful than a 30-year mortgage; able to leap personal challenges in a single bound. I was in total control of my life. How dare something—anything—tug on Super Phil's cape!

But now I was experiencing more than a tug. This was a progress-impeding yank. And it had my attention. This physical challenge was unlike any challenge I had experienced previously. For more than a year prior to this particular early morning wakeup call, I had experienced periodic intestinal problems—aggravating episodes marked by mild to severe stomach cramps, fever and an urgent need to find a bathroom.

In the early days these symptoms would often appear, run their course, then disappear in a matter of days with no systematic treatment whatsoever. Of course, when present, the symptoms were noticeable and unpleasant, but easy for me to rationalize away. Considering my lifestyle as an active person and a busy, traveling professional speaker, I figured these minor physical problems were a direct result of too many late night flights and not enough sleep. Too many greasy fast-food hamburgers and not enough fresh vegetables. Too many professional obligations and not enough personal down time.

Like too many friends, family members, colleagues and even total strangers who find themselves living their equivalent of my life, I chose to ignore the signals my body was sending. I convinced myself that my problems were nothing that a little time off and a few home cooked meals couldn't heal.

However, in the deepest, darkest recesses of my mind there was a nagging concern, a still small voice, telling me that something wasn't right. I couldn't put my finger on exactly what that something was, so in true Super Phil style, I decided to suffer in silence, keeping my little secret to myself, shielding it from public view.

My closest friends, family members and even my wife, had little idea of the scope of my struggle. I was Super Phil! I couldn't let others, even the folks that loved and cared most about me know that I had a weakness, much less where it lay.

So I suffered silently. However, as the weeks turned to months, and those early bouts of intestinal distress became more painful and the occurrences more prolonged, it became obvious that some sort of significant problem existed. That reality became so troubling, that on a couple of occasions I actually mentioned my condition to my wife. Yet, each time my statements were intentionally cloaked in understatement.

"Susan, I don't feel very good today," I would say. "My stomach is bothering me some."

"What's the matter?" she would ask.

"Oh, I've got a case of diarrhea. It must be something I ate."

"Phil, this is the second (or third, or fourth) time you've mentioned this to me. When do you plan to go to the doctor and find out what's going on?"

"Oh, I'll go if it gets any worse," was my predictable response.

Of course, I lied. It did get worse—obviously and progressively worse with each new episode. Several months passed and I never called upon any doctor for help. I was convinced that I just needed to be braver—stronger—for things to get better.

Now, as I continued to sit on that toilet, these unkept promises came flooding back to me. *If this doesn't get better in the next week or two*, I told myself, *I think I will call for a doctor's appointment.* Still I hadn't learned my lesson. Still I hoped for some miracle relief. Still I delayed.

After about twenty minutes alone in the bathroom, I began to feel a little better. The cramping had eased, the nausea had subsided and the diarrhea had stopped for the time being. I needed to clean myself up and get back to bed. Still feeling my way around in the dark, I found the toilet paper roll and dispensed the amount of tissue I thought I needed. Feeling weak and washed out, I worked deliberately, as if in slow motion.

When I had finished the task of cleaning myself I stood and dropped the soiled tissue paper behind me in the direction of the toilet bowl. My aim was usually unfailing. I rarely missed my target—even in the dark. But this time, as I released the paper, I felt it brush against my bare leg. I knew I had missed the mark.

Disgusted, I shuffled away from the toilet bowl, feeling my way along the bathroom counter, toward the door, in search of the light switch. Once located, I flipped the switch and the bathroom was immediately bathed in a painfully bright, blinding light. I closed my eyes tightly and stumbled back toward the toilet. As I did, I gradually eased my eye lids open, blinking rapidly and squinting to allow the acclimation process to take place.

For several seconds, it was hard to see. But as my eyes eventually accepted the light, I scanned the floor for the misplaced toilet tissue and found it lying between the toilet bowl and the shower. As I stooped to pick it up, I noticed the tissue was stained red. Confused, I picked it up and proceeded to drop it into the toilet bowl. Then I noticed the toilet bowl itself. The water in the bowl was a deep scarlet. The color was unmistakable. It was blood. My blood. My heart raced. I was shaken. I was scared. Something was wrong—terribly wrong.

Superman's not supposed to bleed!

2

Anatomy 101

My mind raced as I stood staring in disbelief at the crimson-colored water.

What does this mean? What causes internal bleeding? What other complications might I face?

I was confident that I had read different things over the years about intestinal bleeding. I was even sure that someone I knew had experienced complications from severe internal blood loss. *But who was that? And what was the outcome?* At that precise moment, I just couldn't remember.

Never mind all that now, what does this blood indicate?

My mind searched desperately for quick, definitive answers. But instead of answers, more questions came.

How long have I been bleeding like this? Is this the first time, or has it been going on for weeks—or months—and I've just not been paying enough attention? Is that a lot of blood or does it just look that way to me? How much blood can I afford to lose? Is this a sign of the first —or last—stages of some sort of stomach cancer?

In those first few minutes following discovery, seemingly dozens of random thoughts raced through my mind. I was scared. There was no doubt about it.

Nevertheless even in my frightened state, I quickly recognized the need to regain control of my thoughts and emotions. Had I not, I was convinced my own imagination would have had me dead, buried and forgotten before sunrise. Now was not a time for thoughtless reaction. Now was a time for thoughtful preparation.

As I stood trying to make sense of a situation I had just become aware of, I suddenly became conscious of a solitary bead of sweat as it began its isolated journey high on my bare back, somewhere between my shoulder blades. It trickled slowly at first then, aided by gravity, rolled unimpeded down the concourse of my spine before being absorbed and disappearing into the waistband of my underwear. The sensation caused me to glance up at the image in the bathroom mirror.

There, standing before me was a pitiful reflection of myself. A forty one-year-old man with a receding hairline and an expanding waistline. The image, as if by reflex, caused me to attempt to change my posture somewhat. For a fleeting moment I tried to stand taller, hoping to look the full five feet nine inches I had claimed since high school. But the weight of my current circumstance seemed to cause my shoulders to sag and my upper body to slump noticeably. Honestly, this morning it seemed to me that I looked much shorter—and much older.

The sleek, solid 165-pound athletic build I had carried into my early 30's had eventually given way to a soft, pudgy 202 pounds. In recent days I had noticed a slight reduction in my weight, down to about 189 pounds. I even tried to make myself believe that the weight was coming off for all the right reasons. But the fact remained—and I knew it—the weight loss was a direct result of the on-going battle my body was waging with diarrhea.

The original two hundred plus pounds didn't just sneak up on me. In large part, it was the direct result of more than ten years of almost constant travel, coupled with an ever-increasing sedentary lifestyle. Year after year, I traveled about 150 days annually, eating three plus meals a day in restaurants, fast-food outlets and convenience stores. The meals and snacks were consumed at all hours of the day and night. Like everyone else, I talked about the need to cut down on sweets, fried foods and high fat snacks but talk was about all I did. My chosen lifestyle was not conducive to developing good nutritional discipline.

The weight also added up as my exercise activities began slacking off. Previously I had been physically active, but in recent years I had foregone the racquetball court, the Stairmaster and the early morning runs in favor of a few more minutes with voice mail, email and other busy work. I realized that it was not unusual these days for me to go literally months at a time without so much as breaking a sweat due to any kind of planned physical exercise.

As I gazed at my own reflection in that unforgiving bathroom mirror, I got a good look at myself. I didn't like what I saw.

The nervous perspiration kept coming. Where before I felt a single bead working its way down my spine, now my entire upper body was drenched in sweat. The hair on my chest had already begun to mat due to the accumulating moisture.

The word "perspire" never seemed sufficient to describe what frequently happened to me. I was a serious "sweater." And the sweating I did was not always due to physical exertion or high temperatures. As I grew toward adulthood and independence I learned that nervousness, stress and anxiety could occasionally cause an uncontrolled "sweat response" in me. Situations I did not understand and knew not how to manage were frequent triggers for my involuntary response. Over the years, I had successfully learned to control other telltale signs of personal anxiety such as rapid breathing, fidgeting and quaking voice. However for me, the sweating remained a dead giveaway.

I glanced down at my shirtless, glistening belly.

What's going on in there? Everything looks normal on the outside. What could be so wrong on the inside?

While still pondering questions for which I had no answers, I looked up and into the reflection of my own face. What I saw there unnerved me even more. There, unmistakably etched in my furrowed brow and evidenced by my pained expression, was a frightening combination of fear and worry. I was fearful of what I didn't know or understand and worried about the potential consequences. Once again,

I didn't like what I saw. This time I decided to do something about it. I summoned up all the resolve I could muster. This was a job for Super Phil!

"Phil, get a hold of yourself," I said aloud, in a whispered tone. Somehow actually uttering the words to my mirrored reflection made them more powerful—more emphatic. "Susan will be getting up in a little while and you've got to know how you're gonna handle this thing. Otherwise, she'll be worried sick."

Though the unknowns and dire possibilities signified by the bloody discharge were almost paralyzing, I knew I had to be determined, strong and decisive in the face of these uncertainties. If not for me, for my wife and kids. *Besides,* I kept reminding myself, *there's always the chance that this is just a minor problem.*

By the time I finally left the bathroom, it was approaching 5:30 a.m.

There is no sense in going back to bed now. Susan and the kids will be getting up soon.

Instead, I slipped on a pair of jeans, walked outside and collected the morning paper as usual. I was sitting at the table, scanning its headlines, when Susan made her way into the kitchen a few minutes later.

"Morning," I offered, as I got my first good look at her for the day. Barefoot, dressed in oversized pajamas, standing about five feet two inches tall, she looked slightly taller this particular morning due to an overactive case of "bed hair." On most mornings I would have made some sort of sarcastic comment about how "nice" she looked. She would have lowered her head, while looking up through her eyebrows at me and said something along the lines of, "I'm a real vision, huh? Was this what you were hoping for when you married me?" It would have been just enough to get the day started off with a chuckle. But today I didn't feel like chuckling. Instead, I just left it at "Morning."

"Good morning," she replied softly. "How'd you sleep?"

"Oh, it was just another night."

"You had to get up again, didn't you?" she asked as she turned to face me.

"Yeah," I admitted as I looked back down at the paper spread out before me.

"How many times?" she pressed.

"Four," I said softly.

"Four?"

Susan's voice grew slightly louder, tinged with obvious concern. "Was it diarrhea again?"

"Yeah," I answered still not looking up.

Out of the corner of my eye I saw her turn her back to me as she headed for the coffeepot. Her head was shaking back and forth. Over her shoulder she repeated her all too familiar refrain.

"Phil, you've got to get this thing checked out. Do you want me to call the doctor and make an appointment for you?"

"I'm planning to call him today," I said simply. Then I added casually, "I noticed some blood this morning."

My words stopped her in her tracks. She wheeled to face me. I chose not to look up, keeping my eyes fixed on the newsprint.

"Blood? How much blood?" she asked slowly.

"Enough," I said calmly, trying desperately not to show my own level of concern. "Don't worry. Everything is gonna be all right. I'm sure Dr. Morgan will be able to give me something that will help."

Susan knew I was concerned by the simple fact that after all these months of suffering, I now planned to see a doctor. She had worried about the continuing diarrhea, but now the appearance of blood added an entirely new dimension to the whole issue. It was obvious that Susan wasn't convinced that a quick trip to the doctor would be sufficient to solve my problem. Frankly, neither was I. But it was all the hope I had to cling to for the moment.

"I'll make arrangements to go to the doctor with you," she said.

"No, I'll be fine," I said rather definitively as I began to read the weather forecast out loud.

A couple of hours later, I called our family physician's office and explained to the receptionist that I had a pressing need to see the doctor. "Please tell Dr. Morgan that Phillip Van Hooser would like to see him today if possible. Tell him it's important." She assured me she would pass along the message.

Dr. Glen Morgan specialized in family practice. A quiet, studious man in his early 40's, he had earned my admiration, trust and business, primarily due to his exceptional "bedside manner."

On those rare occasions when I had need of his professional services not once had I found him to be so rushed or busy that he was unable or unwilling to answer my questions. He always seemed as interested in my flu symptoms, infected toe, or hacking cough as I was. His demeanor was thoughtful, thorough and focused. His professional skills were well known and well respected throughout Ocala, Florida, as demonstrated by the large number of people who trusted their healthcare needs to him and his staff. His medical practice was thriving. His advice and care were in great demand.

I appreciated Dr. Morgan for yet another reason. Unlike too

many other physicians today, Dr. Morgan seemed to understand that not everyone's life revolved around a standard nine-to-five doctor's office schedule. Despite his thriving practice and unquestionably busy schedule, he had always gone out of his way to see me on the spur of the moment.

During these periodic visits, he had taken the time to get to know me as a person and had taken an interest in my activities as a professional speaker. He quickly recognized that due to my almost constant travel schedule, it was virtually impossible for me to commit to a doctor's appointment scheduled weeks, or even months in advance. I simply didn't know where I would be.

Therefore, on the few occasions over the years when I had been a little under the weather and preparing for a trip he had massaged his schedule, even to the point of staying past office hours to see me. I was fairly certain, if he got my message that he would do his best to see me as soon as possible. I was right. Within minutes his office staff called back. Dr. Morgan would make time to see me immediately following his last scheduled appointment. At 5:00 p.m. that afternoon I was sitting on an examination table.

"Phil, it's good to see you," Dr. Morgan offered cheerfully as we shook hands.

"It's good to see you, too," I said less enthusiastically. "Thanks for working me in on such short notice, Doc. I really appreciate it."

"Glad I could help." Sensing my obvious, though as yet unspoken concern, the doctor dispensed with the normal idle chitchat. "What's the problem today?"

I hesitated ever so slightly before answering.

Is this really happening? Do I really want to hear what he thinks my problem might be?

The moment was a strange one. I had come seeking his

professional services yet found myself hesitant to share the specifics of what I had just discovered. I was concerned that I didn't know what was going on inside me. But at the same time I was also concerned about what I might soon know. Conflicted, I forged ahead.

"Doc, I've been having some problems recently with diarrhea, stomach cramps, fever, that sort of thing."

As I spoke, Dr. Morgan rolled a small stool directly in front of the examination table on which I was sitting. He took his seat on the stool and leaned forward slightly focusing his full attention on me as I spoke.

"This morning I noticed blood in the toilet bowl. Quite a bit of blood. I figured you'd like to know about that."

"Well, Phil, you figured right. Your physician always needs to know about episodes of internal bleeding. But, first, how long have you been having the diarrhea?"

"For a while now," I answered attempting to be intentionally vague.

The doctor dug deeper.

"How long is 'a while'? A week, two weeks? How long?"

"Longer than that."

"A month, two months?" he persisted.

"Several months now," I answered with a measure of embarrassment. It was already obvious to both of us that this conversation and office visit were long overdue. However, to his credit Dr. Morgan did not deliver the anticipated (and deserved) caregiver's tongue-lashing. As a matter of fact, he wasted no time whatsoever offering critical admonition as to what I *should* have done. Instead, he continued to question and listen. He was on his own mission of discovery.

"What has been your overall general state of health during this period? How have you been feeling?" he asked.

"Honestly? I've felt lousy most of the time," I answered as I began to loosen up and talk straight. "I don't feel this way all the time, but during the tough periods, I have a tremendous amount of cramping and almost constant diarrhea. It's not unusual for me to go to the bathroom ten, twelve, fifteen times during the day. Because of the diarrhea, I'm not sleeping well. I have to get up several times during the night, too. On top of that, I don't have much of an appetite and the tough periods seem to be coming more often and staying with me longer."

"Have you been sick enough that it's caused you to miss any of your speaking engagements?"

"I've been sick enough, but I haven't missed any engagements. There have been several times when I've been on stage speaking and I didn't know if I would be able to make it to the bathroom in time. But I've toughed it out," I said with a little bit more pride than was necessary. "Doc, you know that if I'm not talking, I'm not making any money. I'm a business owner. My family and staff count on me."

"I understand," he said, his words drifted off as he appeared to be lost deep in thought.

I could almost see the wheels turning inside that well-trained brain as he collected the information I shared while postulating, processing, evaluating and discarding what he understood to be the possible causes of my suffering.

"Phil, now about the blood. What was the color of the blood you noticed? Was it a bright red, dark red, or almost black?"

By the specificity of the question, I could tell Dr. Morgan was narrowing down the medical possibilities right on the spot.

"Well, it definitely wasn't black. I would say it was more of a bright red. Why? Does that mean something?"

"Well, Phil, let me say right now that I don't know what's causing the ***hemorrhaging***. That's yet to be determined. But the fact that the blood is bright red in color indicates that it's probably coming from somewhere in the lower sections of the intestinal tract. If it were darker, even black like coffee grounds, that usually means that the blood has been in your system for some time. The longer loose blood remains in your system the more opportunity for the oxygen it's carrying to be depleted, thus causing the blood to change color. In other words, for now the fact that the blood you're noticing is bright red is a good thing. It should make detecting the cause and location of the bleeding a little easier."

Though still concerned, my spirits began to rise. I had done the right thing by seeking the advice of a medical professional, albeit a little late. I was sure the next step would be for Dr. Morgan to reach into his bag of potions and prescribe some sort of miracle medication to quickly solve my little problem. I was feeling more and more confident that I would be as good as new in no time flat.

Even while my optimism was increasing, Dr. Morgan lurched from his perch. Once on his feet, the stool on which he had just been seated rolled harmlessly away from him across the tile floor. The good doctor was immediately engaged in scribbling what appeared to be undecipherable notes into my medical file.

"So what now, Doc?" I asked more cheerfully.

"Well, Phil, the first thing we need to do is get your blood work done ASAP. As soon as we're through here I'm going to make a couple of calls and schedule you to have blood drawn tomorrow morning. That means absolutely nothing to eat or drink after midnight tonight. Understand?"

The professional had taken the wheel and it was time for me to get onboard. "Sure, Doc. That won't be a problem," I replied.

"I also will let the lab know that you need the necessary supplies to gather ***stool samples*** over the next several days."

"Stool samples?"

"That's right, stool samples. It's not a fun job but it is necessary. We need to have an accurate analysis of your ***feces*** to determine exactly how much ***occult***, or non-visible, blood you're losing. Trust me, it's not as bad as it sounds."

That's easy for him to say. He's not in the collection end of this business.

We were obviously making progress.

While still focused on my file, Dr. Morgan continued in a very businesslike, matter-of-fact manner.

"I'm also going to go ahead and start the process of referring you to a local specialist, a ***gastroenterologist***. I want to get you with someone as quickly as possible that knows exactly what he or she is looking at. This is a little bit beyond my area of expertise."

Mere moments before, optimism was growing inside me. Now I suddenly felt a knot of uneasiness form in the very gut where my unknown problem seemed to be in residence.

A specialist? Why do I need a specialist? Does Dr. Morgan know something that he's not sharing? I have to know.

"A specialist? I thought you'd be able to help me. What's going on?" I asked uneasily.

Dr. Morgan turned his full attention to me once again. He could sense my growing anxiety.

"Phil, I am trying to help you. I'm helping you by putting you in touch with people who see this kind of thing every day. Neither you nor I know for sure what is going on down there," he said as he pointed toward my midsection. "These guys know how to figure that out."

Okay, just relax. He's trying to help. Just ask intelligent questions.

"Okay, Doc, that's fair enough. But I have no clue as to what a…whatever you called that guy…does. I've never even heard of such a person."

"Phil, the specialty is ***gastroenterology***, thus a practitioner in the field is a gastroenterologist. A gastroenterologist is a physician specially trained to recognize and treat ***gastrointestinal*** diseases. In layman's terms, these people are experts at understanding what happens in the human body once you put something in your mouth until it comes out the other end."

"So how will they be able to help me?"

"I'll have the results from the blood work and the stool analysis forwarded to your new gastroenterologist, whoever that may be. That person will evaluate the reports and determine what the results indicate and then consult with you. But you're going to have to be patient. Sometimes it takes a while to find an opening for an appointment."

Dr. Morgan paused for a few seconds to allow me time to process this new batch of information. Then almost as an unimportant afterthought, he added, "After the initial consultation, I wouldn't be surprised if they go in there and have a look."

These final words shocked me. I felt my face flush. Perspiration quickly formed on my forehead. This time I couldn't blame my physical reaction on the flu-like symptoms that brought me here in the first place. This physical reaction was unquestionably stress-induced. I tried unsuccessfully to steady my voice.

"You really think they'll need to operate?" I muttered disbelievingly.

"Operate? I never said they would have the need to operate," he responded.

"But you said you wouldn't be surprised if they go inside to have a look."

Dr. Morgan just chuckled at my ignorance.

"You're right, I did say that. But I didn't mean to imply that it would be a procedure requiring surgery. I just assume they will want to perform a ***colonoscopy***. It is ***invasive*** by definition, but it doesn't require surgery. And it is a great tool for identifying specific intestinal problems."

I was certainly glad to hear we weren't discussing surgery, but I was still thoroughly confused. Gastroenterologists, stool samples, colonoscopies, invasion…I needed the good doctor to talk my language for a minute.

"Dr. Morgan, you're gonna have to do better than that. What are you really talking about here?"

"Phil, if it is necessary they will schedule a time to bring you in for an out-patient procedure known as a colonoscopy. The procedure is one in which a flexible lighted fiberoptic tube, or scope, with a camera attachment, is inserted through the ***anus***, up into the ***rectum***, for the purpose of examining the inner linings of your ***large intestine***, or ***colon***. Instead of having to guess what's going on in there, the scope allows them to look for themselves. If there is a problem, they will see it. Of course, during the procedure you will be ***sedated***, making the whole process more tolerable."

Tolerable? Tolerable! According to whom? I've never in my life been "invaded." Certainly not by a computer cable with a searchlight!

Dr. Morgan's explanation of the procedure was concise, thorough and totally rational—still, the mere thought immediately sent cold chills racing up and down my spine.

As a child, I distinctly remember an occasion during which one of my elementary school classmates shared with a group of his peers, in graphic, uncensored detail, his experiences on the receiving end (pardon the pun) of his first enema. The shrieks and groans of my fellow classmates still echo in my ears, drowned out only by the memory of my own shrieks and groans.

How could the medical community sanction such horrendous abuse?

I vowed within myself, then and there, to never allow any such unspeakable horror to befall me. And in the ensuing 35 or so years, none had. Nothing had ever gained entry into my inner rectum, er, I mean sanctum. Now my trusted friend and physician has informed me that a very real possibility existed that I would, in some way, be "roto-rooted" with an instrument of some sort attached to a Polaroid Instamatic camera. The whole scenario, just a few hours earlier would have seemed unfathomable. I just looked at Dr. Morgan in disbelief—and laughed.

He read my mind and smiled.

"Phil, just relax. I realize a lot has been thrown at you today. But don't let your imagination make these things bigger than they are. I assure you, I will see to it that you get the best of care. Just be patient and keep your sense of humor. Worrying won't do you any good. Okay?"

I drew a long breath, shook my head and smiled weakly.

"If you say so, Doc."

“Any last requests?” he asked, before suddenly realizing the possible inappropriate interpretation of his words. He worked quickly to cover his mistake. “I mean is there anything else I can do for you at this point, Phil?”

“Yeah, there is one more thing. This specialist that you will be referring me to. Can you make sure you send me to one who is a human being and not a machine, someone who will be willing to talk me through this thing? I think I’m gonna need all the help I can get.”

Dr. Morgan nodded knowingly.

“Absolutely. I know just the man for you. Dr. Richard Truesdale.”

3

Good News, Bad News

The following few weeks were generally uneventful. I simply followed Dr. Morgan's instructions to a tee—and waited.

After fasting for the required period, I had my blood drawn as scheduled. I received the materials and collection tubes necessary to begin the unenviable process of collecting my own stool samples. Though not necessarily pleasant, the process was quick and painless.

Psychologically, the various activities in which I was involved proved helpful in providing me a focus beyond my physical condition. In some sort of self-encouraging way, offering my blood and collecting the samples made me feel as if I was helping heal myself. The activity was certainly better than sitting by the phone, nervously twiddling my thumbs and worrying myself sicker, waiting for some gastroenterologist's nurse to call with an inconvenient appointment time.

As for my immediate physical condition, it seemed to improve somewhat as I awaited my test results. In the meantime, Dr. Morgan opted not to prescribe any medications until there was a clearer picture of what we were up against. He did, however, share some dietary suggestions he thought might help reduce the immediate effects of diarrhea, cramping and possibly even the bleeding.

He recommended that I suspend indefinitely the ingestion of foods from *my* five basic food groups: Chee-tos, carbonated beverages, barbecue, fried foods of all types and Little Debbie snack cakes. He also warned against high fiber foods like breads made with seeds and coarse cereals such as shredded wheat. In their place he suggested foods like lean meats and fish, instant oatmeal, potatoes and pasta, soups, all types of eggs (except fried), decaffeinated beverages and lots of bananas.

Well, at least I won't starve to death.

I did as instructed.

Thankfully, I began to feel better. My guts seemed to relax, almost as if they were on some well-deserved, long-overdue vacation. Shortly after changing my diet, the diarrhea and cramping subsided greatly. Soon, even the noticeable blood in the toilet bowl disappeared. My dreaded midnight dashes to the bathroom, though still a reality became less frequent. As a result, I rested better and my attitude improved.

I actually began to think that maybe I was on the mend. Maybe just a relatively minor change in my lifestyle was all that was needed.

Better nutrition, less stress and I will be back to my old self in no time flat.

I had no way of knowing that my "old self" no longer existed. In the months ahead, I would experience the physical and psychological process of accepting that fact, as well as creating and living with my "new self."

The telephone was ringing as I approached my desk. I picked up the receiver.

"Hello, thanks for calling Van Hooser Associates. This is Phillip Van Hooser. How can I help you?"

"Mr. Van Hooser, I'm calling from Gastroenterology Associates here in Ocala, Florida. I've been asked to call you to schedule an initial consultation."

"Yeah, I've been expecting your call."

"Well, Mr. Van Hooser, you will be pleased to know we have received and reviewed the results of the tests that Dr. Morgan ordered.

Would you be available to meet with Dr. Truesdale next Wednesday afternoon at 2:30?"

A quick glance at my calendar showed nothing that couldn't be reworked to accommodate the appointment. "Yeah, Wednesday afternoon looks fine," I said.

"Good, we'll see you then."

As my initial appointment with Dr. Truesdale approached, my anxiety level began to increase. Though I had felt somewhat better during the almost two months since my first appointment with Dr. Morgan, in more recent days the nagging symptoms that led me to his office in the first place had returned.

Once again I was making frequent, urgent trips to the bathroom. As a result I had curtailed my eating significantly, reasoning that if less goes in there is less to come out. Hunger pangs were preferable to those gripping cramps. Though the milder, blander foods Dr. Morgan recommended had helped initially, they had not proved to be the cure-all I had hoped and prayed for.

I also had concerns regarding this gastroenterologist. First, I worried whether or not I would hit it off with this new doctor. In many ways, I recognize myself as a throwback to an earlier age. I still believe that connection, communication and compassion, though apparently not as popular as they once were, are still the bedrock of a successful patient/physician relationship.

In my hometown of Princeton, Kentucky, I still remember several times when local Drs. Giannini or Talley would be summoned to our home for a late night house call—and then end up staying for a cup of coffee. Then, as now for many of us, quality health care was spelled T-I-M-E and A-T-T-E-N-T-I-O-N. I worried whether or not this Dr. Truesdale would be one of the new breed of physicians who too often seem to value efficiency over empathy and insurance over information.

Of course I was also worried about the diagnosis itself. My immediate shock had eventually passed since first noticing the blood. Time has a way of lessening the initial impact of any strongly felt human emotion. My initial shock had been replaced by a silent, nagging fear of the unknown. That fear was being fueled by conversations all around me.

It seemed everywhere I turned, I was hearing yet another account of someone suffering from the ravages brought on by various stages of colon cancer. Even more troubling was the fact that those afflicted were not aged and infirmed senior citizens. On the contrary. These were active mothers, fathers, business professionals—the "next door neighbor" types who, in their 30's, 40's and 50's were being afflicted and struck down while their whole lives lay before them. The thought of cancer was significant and weighed heavily on my mind.

I was thirty minutes early. I simply could wait no longer. Susan had volunteered to accompany me to this first appointment intending to offer moral support and serve as a second pair of ears. But as before, I declined her offer. Somehow I felt as if I needed to travel this road alone.

As I entered the office, I immediately noticed the sign beside the receptionist's window: "Sign In." I walked across the lobby to the window and did as the sign instructed. Once there I was greeted by the receptionist who, upon learning of my status as a new patient, loaded me down with a clipboard, pencil and a potpourri of insurance and information forms to be completed. I re-crossed the empty waiting room and settled into a seat along the wall. The paperwork was basic and the distractions few. I finished with time to spare.

Once the paperwork was complete, I returned to the window. The receptionist retrieved the forms, took my insurance card and informed me I would be called as soon as the doctor was ready. I returned to my seat.

The office was not unlike thousands of other such medical

offices around the country. The decor was soft and understated, the colors muted. The chairs lining the walls were far more functional than comfortable.

As I sat visually exploring the room, I could easily imagine how it came to be as it was. In my mind, I pictured some graduate student from some interior decorator's school in New York or Chicago, writing a generic article for some medical practice magazine. The article would propose the calming effects of pastel colors, floral patterns and muted elevator music on anxious office patients. Studies would be quoted as saying 93.1% of all respondents (or some other such unverifiable statistic) claimed to feel more relaxed in such surroundings.

Well maybe so. But not me. I'm one of that 6.9% who would vote for turning the energy level up a notch or two. The calmer and more serene that room felt, the more nervous I became. It reminded me much too much of a funeral home setting. Personally, I would have been much more relaxed and at ease had I been surrounded by vibrant colors and pictures of clowns frolicking on the walls and driving rhythms of The Doobie Brothers' *China Grove* or Tina Turner's rendition of *Proud Mary*.

And like every other medical office I had ever set foot in, there were piles and piles of magazines from months—sometimes years—gone by. Magazines that in a different situation, I would never have given a second glance. Yet with nothing but time on my hands they somehow seemed inviting.

As I began sorting through the offerings I happened upon a small two-color brochure with the cover title, *Gastroenterology Associates of Ocala* and *The Ocala Endoscopy ASC*. Curious, I picked the brochure up and began thumbing through its pages. It quickly became obvious that the brochure had been created to answer the most basic of questions from patients like me. Questions dealing with office hours, appointments, fees, billing and insurance, as well as after-hours emergencies. (Nowhere did I find a section on house calls.)

However, one section of the brochure caught my attention. The section was simply labeled "Doctors." Under this heading two simple paragraphs told me some of what I needed to hear. The first paragraph read:

Dr. Rumalla, Dr. Maxwell, Dr. Van Eldik, Dr. McClary, Dr. Barish and Dr. Truesdale have been specialty trained and are all certified diplomats of the American Board of Gastroenterology and the American Board of Internal Medicine. All of the doctors function as consultants in the field of Gastroenterology (digestive diseases). They do not function as Internists or Primary Care Physicians.

Good! At least my new doctor and his listed colleagues had earned some elevated credentials and professional identification. Of course, I had no idea what these credentials meant, or even if they were legitimate. But at least these guys seemed awfully proud of them and that, to me, seemed to be a good start.

The second paragraph continued:

Although we operate as a group practice, each doctor has his own group of patients. You, as a patient, will be able to see the same doctor each time. This consistency preserves a continuity of care and helps to firmly establish a secure, working doctor-patient relationship. In the event of a medical emergency, if your doctor is not available, one of the other doctors will have access to your medical files and can promptly attend to your medical needs.

So they had no plans for making me change horses in midstream.

I will be seeing the same doctor each time. That's a good thing.

I've always believed that a man should have one good woman, one good dog and one good car on which to lavish his full attention. Multiples of any of these tend to complicate life unnecessarily. I feel the same holds true for a doctor. It just takes too long and requires too much effort to break a new one in. One good one is plenty.

As I flipped to the next page of the brochure I noticed pictures and professional biographies of the six doctors. A couple of things struck me immediately. First, they were all smiling. Every one of them. That was another good thing.

I have discovered that when doctors frown, the patient usually doesn't enjoy what happens next. I remember going to my dentist's office once to have a tooth checked. After just a couple of minutes of silently inspecting my choppers, I heard him grunt unintelligibly to the dental hygienist and then, out of the corner of my eye I saw him frown. Approximately ninety excruciatingly painful minutes later, I climbed out of that dental chair, minus one of my "big teeth," as my youngest daughter calls them. Only then did I see my dentist smile. I now prefer to see my doctor and dentist smile early on.

The other thing I noticed about these six was they all looked like me. Not literally, of course. But each of the six looked to be in his 40's. That encouraged me. I reasoned that they could better understand me, my condition, my life and my concerns if they were experiencing the same general life issues at the same time I was experiencing them.

Of the six doctors, Dr. Richard A. Truesdale, Jr., was listed last. His picture depicted a handsome man in his mid 40's with an angular face and a full head of dark hair. His biography read simply:

Dr. Richard A. Truesdale, Jr., graduated from Northeastern University, College of Pharmacy, in Boston in 1973. In 1976, he received his Masters Degree from the University of Florida. He graduated from George Washington University, School of Medicine at Washington, D.C., in 1983. Both his Internal Medicine training and Fellowship in Gastroenterology, were completed at Walter Reed Army Medical Center in Washington, D.C. He moved to Ocala and joined our office in July 1992. He was certified as a Diplomat of the American Board of Internal Medicine in 1986 and the American Board of Gastroenterology in 1991.

As I finished reading the biography and before I had time to digest its implications, the door to the inner examination rooms swung open and an attractive, dark-haired young woman in nurse garb emerged.

"Mr. Van Hooser, my name is Carla Zimmerman, Dr. Truesdale's assistant. I think we're ready for you. You can follow me."

As I stood to join her, I suspected immediately we would get along well. In those first few seconds I recognized not only her professionalism, but I sensed she liked to smile. As I followed her to the scales, I felt the butterflies beginning to reassemble in my stomach. Once my baseline weight had been determined and recorded, Carla led me into one of the separate exam rooms where she checked my blood pressure and heart rate. I answered her few basic questions before she prepared to leave me to wait alone for Dr. Truesdale.

I suppose she sensed my growing anxiety because on her way out the door she once again smiled warmly and said, "You're going to like Dr. Truesdale. I've been with him for several years. He's the best."

I certainly hope so.

In less than two minutes, before I could worry much more, the examination room door reopened and in walked a gentleman wearing a tie and a white lab coat. A yellow file folder was tucked under his arm. I recognized him immediately. He looked just like his picture. And he was smiling.

A good sign!

"Mr. Van Hooser, I'm Dr. Truesdale," he said as he extended his hand.

I took his outstretched hand and we shook. My attempts to size up the man began immediately. He seemed friendly and out-going enough. I sensed a measure of professional confidence, but no arrogance. He seemed comfortable in his surroundings.

As a result, I felt more comfortable, too. He was taller than I by four or five inches, but I estimated we probably weighed about the same. I got no initial indication of any feelings of superiority on his part.

First impressions being what they are, so far so good.

"It's nice to meet you, Doctor," I said simply.

With that, Dr. Truesdale pulled up a stool and took his seat. He laid the yellow file folder on a single shelf that extended from the wall. He was ready to go to work.

"Mr. Van Hooser," he began.

I interrupted, "Please call me Phil."

"Okay, Phil. I have received the results from the tests you have been taking and the notes from your meeting with Dr. Morgan several weeks ago. I can see here you've been having these problems for some time now. Diarrhea. Blood. All the good stuff. How are you feeling now?"

"I'm not doing quite as bad as when I first saw Dr. Morgan, but I have felt better."

He smiled. "I'll bet so," he said. "Listen, Phil, before you leave the office today we will take a careful medical and personal history. However, you need to understand that this kind of problem is frustrating in that we can't really tell what's going on down there by taking your temperature and listening to your heart. We've got to get in there and take a look around to know for sure. Did Dr. Morgan mention anything to you about the possibility of a colonoscopy?"

"As a matter of fact, he did. And from what little I heard, it sounds like one of those things I would just as soon pass on, if you don't mind." I tried to chuckle, but due to my nervousness, my laughter sounded more like a pitiful squeak. Dr. Truesdale just nodded. I could only imagine how many hundreds of anxious first-time patients he had encountered just like me.

"Well, you came here to see if I can help you. For me to help you, I've got to see what's going on in there. So, I'm going to schedule the procedure for March 19th. That's next Thursday at 10:30 a.m. Will that work for you?"

"Yeah, I think so," I said less than enthusiastically.

Truesdale continued.

"Phil, let me take a minute to tell you what to expect. First, I hope you will believe me when I tell you the procedure is not as bad as it sounds. You will be conscious but sedated throughout and should feel no pain at all. You may feel a little pressure in your gut while we're in there, but no pain. Frankly, with the level of sedation we normally administer, I doubt that you'll remember anything about the experience once it's over. Following the procedure, we will continue to monitor your condition for about an hour just to make sure everything is okay. From start to finish, you will be with us about three hours or so. After that, you will be able to head home.

"The toughest part of the procedure actually happens the day and night before. On the day before the colonoscopy is scheduled, you can only have clear liquids. It's important that your colon be clean and well prepared before we start the procedure. That means about all you can have is fat-free broth, coffee—without creamer—tea, water and all the light colored Popsicles you can eat."

The thought of gorging myself at a Popsicle buffet made me smile. "I haven't eaten a Popsicle in years," I said.

"Well, you might want to try one, because it will taste like prime rib compared to what comes next."

"Oh, great," I replied sarcastically. "What's that?"

"On the evening before the procedure, you will need to drink a gallon of the prescribed ***colon prep***."

"A full gallon?"

"That's right. A full gallon. Once you start, you will need to drink an eight-ounce glassful of the prep every 10-15 minutes until you drain the jug. I'll tell you right now, it's not very tasty but it is necessary. When you finish it, just know the worst is over. The next day is easy compared to drinking this stuff. Oh, yeah, one friendly piece of advice. I highly recommend you start drinking the prep pretty early in the evening. Remember, what goes in must come out. If you start drinking it too late you will be up all night running to the bathroom."

I've been up all night running to the bathroom for months! That's why I'm here in the first place.

"Phil, please understand that a good colon prep is critical to a successful examination. To find out what's wrong, we've got to do this thing right. No short cuts, okay?"

"I understand," I replied.

"The next morning come at your scheduled time and bring your wife with you. Since you will be sedated during the procedure, she will need to drive you home. As far as the procedure itself, I'll be doing the driving. Okay?"

"I guess it sounds pretty straightforward," I said. "But how long will it be after the procedure is over until we know what the problem is?"

"Oh, don't worry about that. It shouldn't take long at all. I should be able to tell you and your wife what's going on before you leave the office to go home."

"Really? Well, I'm glad to hear that," I replied. "I'm ready to get this thing under control."

"I know you are," he replied somewhat empathetically. "Have you got any other questions for me now?"

"None that I can think of," I said.

"Well then, I'll see you back here on the 19th."

I left the office with a great deal more confidence than when I entered. Dr. Truesdale had met and even exceeded my initial expectations. Our conversation had been casual. He had taken the time to outline what I should expect and to make sure I understood the procedure. I got the real sense that he cared.

I returned to the Endoscopy Center on the morning of March 19, 1999, two days after celebrating my 42nd birthday. Dr. Truesdale had proven himself to be a man of his word. The colon prep was, in fact, the worst tasting swill imaginable. I gulped down each putrid eight-ounce helping in chug-a-lug fashion to keep from gagging and retching. Half the time I gagged and retched anyway. But drink it I did. The whole gallon. Every stomach-churning drop.

And again, true to the doctor's word, all the liquid that went in came back out—in torrents. For two or three hours during the previous evening, my time had been consumed with "drinking and dashing." Drinking the colon prep, then dashing for the bathroom. My kids, then ages 11, 8 and 3, thought it was great fun to see dear old Dad doing what is commonly known around our house as the "Tennessee Trot." After a little while, I decided to cut out the middleman entirely and just drink the concoction while remaining in the bathroom, thereby eliminating travel time.

Eventually I fulfilled my objective. Dr. Truesdale had stated he wanted an absolutely clean colon. After more than two and a half-hours of literal and figurative flushing, I was convinced my colon was as clean as the proverbial hound's tooth. I went to bed with a clear conscience—and a clear colon. My colon was ready for public inspection.

March 19th dawned bright and beautiful in central Florida, one of those days the Chamber of Commerce just smiles about. But there was more on my mind than warm sun and tropical breezes. The time had come, once and for all, for me to find out what had been ailing me.

Susan and I arrived at the Endoscopy Center at 9:30 a.m., a full hour before my scheduled 10:30 a.m. colonoscopy. By 9:50 a.m. all the required release forms had been signed and I was being led off to the changing area. Before I left, Susan gave me a quick reassuring hug and kiss. She reminded me that she loved me and would be waiting for me when the procedure was finished. I tried to read her face for signs of concern. I figured they were there, but I could see none. That made me smile. We were both concerned. We hoped and prayed the news we would soon receive would be good. But whatever the news, I was sure Susan was already prepared to be strong and supportive.

The next thing I knew, I found myself in a little locker room area. Once there the attendant gave me a lock and key, along with one of those ever-stylish, backless hospital gowns. I was instructed to get undressed and slip on the gown. The locker was provided for my clothes and valuables. Once my belongings were placed in the locker and secured, the key would be delivered to Susan for safe keeping until it was time for me to once again get dressed. Soon I was parading barefoot across a cold tile floor, headed to my assigned hospital bed. I felt a draft.

To my surprise there were probably ten to twelve other folks like me being attended to in preparation for *their* intestinal inspection. That proved to be a bit of an eye-opener for me. As foolish as it sounds now, that was really the first time I realized that others might be going through the same thing I was. To that point, in my mind, I was a totally isolated case. I suppose I was working under the misguided assumption that I was the only person in America who had such a problem; that this whole medical specialty had been developed specifically for me. My naivete proved there was much I had to learn.

I crawled into my assigned bed. The attendant drew the curtains closed around me on three sides. Just before she left me, she encouraged me to get comfortable, reminding me my nurse would be with me shortly.

Get comfortable? Yeah, right! Here I lay half-naked, surrounded by total strangers, preparing to have a flashlight shoved up my rear end. I can't see why in the world I would need to work at being comfortable.

Difficult as it was, I kept my sarcastic thoughts to myself.

A couple of minutes later, as promised, my nurse appeared. However it wasn't Carla. I was surprised and a bit disappointed.

"Hello there," this stranger offered, cheerfully.

"Hi," I responded obligingly. "Where's Carla? I thought she was Dr. Truesdale's assistant."

"Oh, she is. But she works exclusively with him in the office. I and a couple of other nurses work with him on the procedures."

I'm certain she sensed my concern, but she continued.

"I'm sorry, I haven't met you yet. What's your name?" she asked.

"Phillip Van Hooser."

As I mentioned my name, she smiled broadly.

"So you're Phillip Van Hooser. I have heard so much about you."

"You have?" I asked.

"Sure. You are Phillip Van Hooser, the speaker, aren't you?"

"Yeah, but how did you know that?"

"Several months ago you did a leadership presentation at the company where my husband works. He was *so* impressed! He came home and told me all about you and your talk. He even told me some of the stories you shared. I've never seen him quite that excited after attending a meeting."

"Thanks for telling me that. It's always nice to hear from someone who appreciates my work. I wish I could tell you that I remember him, but I meet a lot of people…"

"That's no problem. He sure remembers you. And now I get to meet you, too."

Her enthusiasm—and flattery—made me feel much better. For the moment, I even forgot what I was facing.

"So you've been having some problems," she said. "Let me tell you what you can expect from this colonoscopy. I will be administering a sedative in a few minutes. After it takes effect you will still be awake, but will be pretty much out of it. We will then take you into the procedure room where they will pump your colon up with gas so Dr. Truesdale can get a better look when he goes in with the scope. Then Dr. T. does his thing and you will be back in here in no time. Any questions?"

"Yeah, one. About this sedative. Are there different strengths that can be administered?" I asked.

"Yes, there are. Why do you ask?"

"Well, if at all possible, I would like to know what's going on during the procedure. I understand there will be a screen that will show the image of the inside of my colon during the procedure. I would like to watch what's happening and I would like to be able to remember what I've seen. If possible, I just don't want to be out of it."

"Are you sure? The sedative is intended to block the pain."

"I understand. I'm not trying to be John Wayne or anything like that. Believe me, I want more than a piece of leather to bite on. I'm just asking if I can try and get by with a smaller dose. Once they get in there, then if I can't stand the pain, just give me more. Okay?"

"I'll check with Dr. T."

The nurse returned a few minutes later. "Dr. Truesdale said, 'If that's what Phil wants, okay.' So, let's take you on down."

Upon arriving in the procedure room, the sedation was administered. Within minutes, I was feeling light-headed and very relaxed, but still aware of my surroundings. Dr. Truesdale entered the room and was hovering around some expensive looking equipment.

"It's no use, buddy, I recognize you," I said, my inhibitions melting away as the sedative took hold. "You're the one who made me drink a gallon of camel spit."

Truesdale just chuckled. "Yeah, but it looks like you're a survivor. By the way, they tell me you want to try to tough this out, right?"

"Right."

"That's fine with me. But if you get too uncomfortable, just let me know and we will get you some more joy juice."

"It's a deal," I said.

About that time Dr. Truesdale's assistant approached and had me roll over on my left side. Directly in front of me was a television monitor. Dr. Truesdale, positioned behind me, instructed me to bend my right leg and thrust it forward as far as I could. As I did I felt the doctor untying the strings on the gown that helped shield my dignity. As the strings released a cool breeze swept over my now bare and exposed backside.

"Phil, are you ready?" Dr. Truesdale asked.

"As ready as I ever will be."

At that instant, I felt pressure in my lower abdomen. Suddenly a picture of sorts appeared on the screen before me. There, in living color, was a 19-inch, high definition image of the lining of my colon--revealed.

The eagle has landed!

For the next few minutes, Dr. Truesdale worked very deliberately as he carefully maneuvered the scope into my anal canal, through my lower rectum and into the upper reaches of my colon. It had been explained earlier to me that this was a safe procedure, but not completely without risk. The greatest risk I was told, and the one I now recognized Dr. Truesdale working to avoid, was the risk of tearing or perforating the colon itself with the instrument. If that were to happen, the contents of the colon would leak or seep out into the otherwise sterile body cavity and the results could be deadly. Dr. Truesdale was out to find the cause of my problems, but he wasn't about to rush and make a mistake.

While he worked, the screen displayed an unblinking picture of what the scope was encountering. Dr. Truesdale tried to offer a running play-by-play description of what we were seeing on the screen and at the same time check my condition.

"How you doing, Phil?"

"Okay so far."

"All right, we are passing through the rectum right now and will begin working our way up though the ***sigmoid*** portion of the colon into what is referred to as the ***descending colon***. Notice the veins and red color of the lining. That's what a healthy colon looks like. You still comfortable?" he asked as he continued to probe deeper.

"I'm not really comfortable, but I'm still with you."

"Just bear with me, Phil. I want to go up as far as I can while we are in here," he said with an encouraging tone. Then the scope stopped and focused on one discolored section of lining. The doctor's tone of voice changed. I could tell he was no longer speaking to me. The conversation was now with himself and with his assistant.

"Uh, oh. There it is. That's what I was afraid of."

There what is? What were you afraid of?

"I'm going to take a ***biopsy*** of that area there and the other one just beyond it. Okay, got it. Phil, I'm going to try to make this turn into the ***transverse colon***. This is going to hurt more, but I really need to see what's around the corner. Do your best to stay with me."

Again, Dr. Richard Truesdale proved himself to be an honest man. The pain increased exponentially as he fished the tube around the corner and deep into the recesses of my ***bowels***. Again, he noticed other areas of concern. As for me, my attention was no longer on the screen. My more immediate concern was the pain I was experiencing. I didn't know how much more I could tolerate. I was just on the verge of begging for more medication when I heard him say, "That's enough. I've seen all I need to see. Relax, Phil. It will be over in just a few seconds."

The scope was retracted quickly and the screen returned to its blank form. The pressure and pain were gone. The entire experience, from entry to exit, had taken only twenty minutes or so.

"Phil, you did great," the doctor said, as he gave me a reassuring pat. "Rest for a little while and I will talk to you in about an hour." Then he left the room.

About an hour later, I had dressed and rejoined Susan in a waiting area. Maybe it was the lingering effect of the sedatives still in my system, but I was very calm as we readied ourselves for our debriefing with Dr. Truesdale. We didn't have long to wait. Dr. Truesdale entered the room and pulled up a chair along side of us.

"Mrs. Van Hooser, it is nice to meet you. Your husband was a trooper in there," he began. "Phil, how you feeling?"

"A little weak and hungry," I replied.

"That's a good sign. We will be finished here shortly. Have your wife take you out for a nice lunch. You deserve it."

Enough of the idle chatter, what did you find?

"Well, folks, let me get right to it. I've got some good news and I've got some bad news. First, the good news. Phil, you will be happy to know that you almost certainly don't have colon cancer. We will send the biopsies to a pathologist, but we feel sure they will come back clean."

What a relief! That was my greatest concern. But, what's this bad news he's talking about?

"Well, if I don't have cancer, what is the problem?" I asked.

"That's the bad news. You most certainly do have ***ulcerative colitis***. From all your symptoms and the results of the tests you took, I feared it. Today, the colonoscopy confirmed it."

"Ulcerative colitis? I've never even heard of that before. What are you talking about?" I asked.

“Ulcerative colitis is a chronic, incurable disease that causes inflammation of the inner lining of the colon and rectum. It’s a form of what we refer to as ***inflammatory bowel disease***, or ***IBD***. We don’t know what causes it and why one person gets it and another person doesn’t. What we do know is that it is a tricky disease. People like yourself who suffer from it alternate between flare-ups and periods of remission throughout their lives.

“However, now that we know what we’re up against, I will be starting you on a combination of medication and diet that will hopefully manage the symptoms of the ulcerative colitis and significantly increase the time between the ***flare-ups***. Phil, we cannot cure this disease with medication, but hopefully we can control it somewhat. I will also want to see you on a regular basis for checkups.

“Phil, the bad news is that you’re going to have to keep fighting this thing. And there are sure to be some tough times. On the other hand, the good news is that now you won’t have to fight it alone. We’re going to do everything in our power to help you. Starting now.”

4

Doing What Has To Be Done

It's an incredible phenomenon once you begin to consider the almost unbelievable impact that words—simple words—can have on the balance of your life. Without fully recognizing—or accepting—it at the time, words can serve as the catalyst of change that redirects the course of your life completely. Like it or not.

"You most certainly do have ulcerative colitis...Ulcerative colitis is a ***chronic****, incurable disease..."*

Though I didn't recognize it immediately, Dr. Truesdale's words would set into motion changes in my life and in the life of my family that I could neither imagine nor reverse. The words the doctor spoke to us were unexpected and frankly, unwelcome. We didn't want to hear what we heard. But once the words were heard, our life was immediately impacted and bound to change forever.

I don't remember an overpowering sense of shock or dread descending upon me in that office that day. Maybe the relaxing effects of the sedative were still at work in my mind and body. Maybe the words themselves caused me to be numb to my own feelings. Or maybe I was still focused on being Superman. Whatever the case, it took a while for the gravity of the diagnosis to sink in.

Before leaving the office, Dr. Truesdale provided written material for us to review. He explained that in an effort to control and manage this disease, we would be initiating a combination of medication and diet. He knew what I would soon learn. The treatment of ulcerative colitis and IBD is an inexact science at best. Each case as unique and different as the personality of the individual sufferer. In the days ahead we would begin the laborious process of isolating and determining the best course of medical treatment for me.

Over lunch, a little later, Susan and I began the process of coming face-to-face with this new reality for our lives and how we would choose to handle it. We quickly realized that definitive plans and decisions needed to be made.

"Phil, how are you feeling?" Susan asked over her salad.

"I feel fine physically," I offered somewhat dejectedly. "But it's really hard for me to believe that I've got some sort of incurable disease."

"Well, Dr. Truesdale seems very confident in his test results. We've got the answer to the first question. We know what the problem is. Now the big question is what are you planning to do about it."

Her voice was even, yet compassionate. Her words, coupled with the look in her eyes, made me know she was ready to help do whatever needed to be done. But she needed direction that only I could provide. For her to determine how *she* would handle my newfound illness, she first needed to know how *I* intended to handle it. It was a critical time of decision for both of us.

Her question produced its desired effect. It got me thinking. For the next couple of minutes I silently weighed a number of random thoughts and the emotions they elicited.

How could this happen? Why is it happening to me? Is it something I should have noticed earlier? I'm a young man, with a young family. How is this going to affect us? How is this going to affect my business?

These and similar thoughts raced through my mind. As Susan waited patiently for me to respond, I felt a knot beginning to form in the pit of my stomach. The knot had nothing to do with my current physical condition. This knot was a direct result of my current emotional distress. Then it hit me! Thankfully, I recognized exactly what was happening to me.

As a result of all this newfound, discouraging information that had been thrust upon me, I was beginning the process of worrying. All of the unknowns associated with my condition and their effect on me were beginning to accumulate—to pile up—causing me to worry. As strange as it may sound, this realization that worry had suddenly entered the picture brought one more, very specific thought into my consciousness. This thought was a welcome one. One that had an overall calming effect, equal to that of a visit from a dear old friend.

The thought itself was derived from a particular training concept I had developed, and then spoken and written about dozens of times during the preceding ten years. But for me personally, it was more than a mere concept. For more than twenty-five years, it had served as a personal philosophy which I enthusiastically embraced and to which I had doggedly adhered. The thought?

Worry is unproductive use of one's imagination. If worry is unproductive use of one's imagination, then planning is productive use of one's imagination. Therefore, if something is worth worrying about, it's worth planning for. If it's not worth planning for, why worry about it?

For me, this concept has always seemed both elementary and liberating. It reminds me that, in essence, there is no need to worry, one way or the other. If something is of great enough concern to me, I need to get busy planning what I will do to either remedy the situation completely or at least lessen its impact. Worry is not required. On the other hand, if I'm *unable* to create a viable plan to remedy a situation completely or to lessen its impact—or I'm *unwilling* to do anything productive about the situation—what good will worrying do? Just let it happen. Let it take care of itself. Don't worry—be oblivious.

With my spirit suddenly buoyed by this thought, I turned my conscious attention to planning and to Susan.

"Before I tell you what I'm going to do," I heard myself saying, "let me tell you what I'm not going to do. I see no benefit in getting a lot of other people involved right now. We'll just keep it between ourselves and tell others as the need arises. Agreed?"

"Agreed," Susan said.

"Another thing I'm not going to do—I'm not going to feel sorry for myself. I don't know how or why this is happening to us. But we both believe the Bible teaches that everything happens for a reason, and that good can come out of difficulties. So we need to look for the positives wherever we can find them."

"I'm with you," she said.

"Finally, I think we need to learn as much about ulcerative colitis and IBD as we can. What scares me most right now is not what I know, but what I don't know. I just need to understand this disease better."

Susan seemed encouraged by my attitude. "Phil, you know I'll help you do what has to be done. We'll get through this together."

The next few weeks were spent gathering as much information as I could about ulcerative colitis and IBD. Dr. Truesdale provided some helpful information and various sources, while I spent additional hours reading and searching the Internet. What I learned was informative and eye opening while, at the same time, rather discouraging.

I learned that Inflammatory Bowel Disease or IBD as many refer to it, is a term which refers to both ulcerative colitis and ***Crohn's disease***. Basically, ulcerative colitis causes ***inflammation*** of the superficial layers (the ***mucosa***) of the large intestine (colon), including the rectum. This inflammation is restricted to the colon and is known to have a fairly even and continuous distribution throughout the affected areas.

Crohn's disease, on the other hand, commonly causes inflammation of the innermost lining of the large and/or ***small***

intestine, but can also affect the upper gastrointestinal tract, including the esophagus and stomach. When inflammation (or flare-ups) occur, the lining of the intestinal wall swells, becomes ***ulcerated*** and bleeds.

I was totally unaware that there are estimated to be between one and two million American sufferers. Yet no one knows what causes IBD. Two prevalent theories suggest the causes are either ***genetic*** (15-30% of the patients with IBD have a relative with the disease), or related to changes in the body's ***immune system*** (the body's natural defense against disease). Virtually no evidence exists to indicate that stress causes IBD. The medical research community believes that high levels of stress tend to complicate the symptoms associated with IBD and therefore, makes the condition more difficult to manage. At the present time there is no known cure.

I read with interest that most IBD cases are diagnosed before age 30, but that no age is immune. Pre-schoolers, as well as senior citizens, may develop the disease at virtually any age.

The physical problems of ulcerative colitis manifest themselves when inflammation of the colon and rectum keeps water from being absorbed into the bloodstream and results in diarrhea. Additional common symptoms include abdominal cramps and ***rectal bleeding***. Some people may experience heightened levels of fatigue, weight and appetite loss, ***anemia***, joint pain and liver problems. Ulcerative colitis is marked by periods of ***remission*** (during which one recovers from feeling ill and begins to feel well) and flare-ups (periods during which the colitis is active).

About half of all ulcerative colitis sufferers experience severe symptoms, occasionally requiring periods of hospitalization to stop severe diarrhea and blood loss and to correct ***malnutrition*** (resulting from severe diarrhea).

The risk of colon cancer is higher with ulcerative colitis patients who have suffered with the disease for an extended period of time (ten years or longer). Eventually, one third of all ulcerative colitis patients are forced to have their colons surgically removed—the ultimate cure for the problem.

Crohn's disease is more troublesome still. The most common symptoms are pain in the abdomen (often the lower right side), diarrhea and weight loss. Chronic bleeding commonly results in anemia. Children who suffer from Crohn's disease may experience delayed physical development and even stunted growth. Difficult complications can arise in Crohn's patients, such as scar tissue forming on intestinal walls, causing intestinal passages to become smaller until they eventually close completely.

Additionally, ***fistulas*** (abnormal channels) commonly form when ***ulcers*** break through the intestinal wall and continue tunneling into surrounding healthy tissues of the bladder, vagina or skin. These fistulas frequently occur around the anus and rectum.

Two-thirds of Crohn's patients will eventually require surgery to reduce severe symptoms or complications. But unlike ulcerative colitis, surgery is no cure for Crohn's disease. Many of these surgical patients will require additional surgery to control their conditions.

The more I learned, the more studious I became. As difficult as my condition was to accept, I was reminded by both my research and by my regular conversations with Dr. Truesdale that things could always be worse—much worse. Therefore, if IBD was to be my fate, I needed to know what I was up against in the present and what I could expect in the future.

My monthly appointments with Dr. Truesdale offered me the opportunity to continue my gastroenterological education. The good doctor monitored my condition closely and carefully explained the need to find the proper mix of medication, nutrition and positive emotional support. He warned that over time, being "sick and tired" of being "sick and tired" could have a devastating effect on one's emotional well being. Therefore each aspect of my treatment was intended to lessen both the physical *and* emotional effects of IBD.

He carefully explained that, though new treatments were being developed and introduced regularly, the medications currently available to treat my condition were fairly limited and fell into one of three categories.

The first category focused on ***steroids***. ***Cortisone*** and ***Prednisone*** both serve as powerful steroids used to arrest the development of an acute IBD flare-up. Each normally begins with a high initial dosage intended to bring the flare-up under almost immediate control. Eventually the dosages are tapered back until a low maintenance level can be determined. As a general rule, in the short term these drugs work very well. However, if continued for extended periods, these specific medications are known to produce significant adverse side effects of their own.

The second category of treatment ***medications*** available involved anti-inflammatory drugs such as ***mesalamine*** (***Asacol***, ***Pentasa*** and ***Rowasa***), ***sulfasalazine*** (***Azulfidine***) and ***olsalazine*** (***Dipentum***). These drugs work to reduce the onset of flare-ups and tend to be tolerated well by the body over extended periods of time.

Finally, the third category of treatment for IBD sufferers was the immune system ***suppressors***. Because it is commonly believed that an overactive immune system plays some role in causing ulcerative colitis, certain drugs are prescribed as a means of suppressing the human immune system. At times, these drugs prove to be effective. Included in this group are ***azathioprine*** (***Imuran***), ***6-MP*** (***Purinethol***), ***cyclosporine*** (***Neoral, Sandimmune***) and ***methotrexate*** (***Rheumatrex***).

Dr. Truesdale started me on measlamine and prednisone (anti-inflammatory medications) coupled with a low-fiber diet. The initial treatment regime produced hope, but in the end, not very much success. Over the four-week interval between the formal diagnosis and my next appointment, little improvement in my overall condition was recorded. I continued to experience episodes of diarrhea, though somewhat less frequent and slightly less painful. Not pleased with the overall progress we were experiencing, Dr. Truesdale continued to explore other possibilities.

Over the ensuing seventeen-month period, we experimented with a number of different combinations of medications and diets. During that time I consumed countless pills—at one point forty individual tablets each day—and, frankly, little else.

I expected the diet part of the healing equation to be the most difficult for me. I loved to eat. I always have. I loved the taste of red meat, spicy foods and vegetables saturated in pork fat. I cut my teeth (and taste buds) in a large Southern family that practiced the philosophy, "If it ain't fried—it ain't fit to eat." But all those years of carefree consumption came to a screeching halt with the onset of ulcerative colitis.

Initially, I tried to continue eating all the things that I loved so well—but I couldn't. They hurt me too much. My gut just couldn't tolerate them any longer. So when the doctor recommended that we experiment with various diets, not for the purpose of losing weight, but rather to see which my colon would respond to best, I was surprisingly willing.

For weeks at a time, I tolerated low residue/low fiber diets, followed by diets high in fiber and bran. I spent one especially grueling twenty-one day period without ingesting one morsel or drop of anything resembling a dairy product. The concern relative to possible lactose intolerance was eventually proven to be unfounded. I tried fruits and vegetables, then discontinued fruits and vegetables. I eliminated fried foods (almost) completely. Week after frustrating week the monotonous process of diet isolation, then elimination, continued.

Over time, I saw no noticeable difference as to how my body responded to one particular type of diet as compared to another. I was able, however, to identify individual foods that I tolerated better (or worse) than others. For example, the single food item that caused me the least amount of gastrointestinal distress was a plain turkey sandwich on wheat. As a result I ended up eating hundreds of them, occasionally for breakfast, lunch and dinner.

The worst tolerated single item? Carbonated beverages of all types. I soon found myself regularly opting for water with lemon, along with a sugar substitute, as my drink of choice. My gut was happier *and* so was my wallet—I was saving anywhere from $1.25 to $2.00 off each lunch or dinner tab!

Throughout this period of extended treatment experimentation, I remained as hopeful, optimistic and upbeat as I possibly could. I had to. What else could I do? Though my condition at times was as bad or worse than it had been when first discovered, I had no other option. I worked to become the model patient. When Dr. Truesdale prescribed a specific course of treatment, I stayed with the plan religiously until he decided a change was necessary.

I owe a tremendous debt of gratitude to Dr. Truesdale. By way of his professional demeanor and personal touch, he quickly earned my unwavering respect and confidence. As a result, I granted him an unprecedented level of trust. The treatment decisions that were made, we made together with a clear explanation and understanding of not only the "whats, hows and whens," but also the "whys."

I will forever be grateful that our monthly appointments were more dialogues than monologue, with questions, observations and input offered by both of us. I give Dr. Truesdale the credit he deserves for allowing these periodic office visits to evolve into casual conversations carefully crafted to identify the problems of the body, but equally important, the concerns of the mind.

I have never understood why intelligent, educated, functioning individuals (patients) would allow their relationship with professional caregivers (physicians) to be so blatantly one-sided. Yet I have heard what I consider to be horror stories from friends, family members, even relative strangers, as they recounted experiences where their physicians could be described as having been indifferent, cold, inattentive, belligerent, contentious, offensive, haughty, rude, domineering, contemptuous and unresponsive, to name a few.

Why? Why would physicians choose to act in such an

unprofessional manner in the first place? And equally important, why do patients take it?

Here is some carefully thought out advice for those folks who wish to improve the quality of physical and emotional care they receive from their caregivers. If you don't get the quality of treatment, attention and time you think you deserve—that you (or your insurance policy) are paying for—speak these words loud and clear to the offending individual, "You're fired!" That's right! In America you have the right to fire someone who is not providing the level of satisfaction that you are paying for. End the relationship now and go find someone who will be able to satisfy your physical and emotional needs.

I can only imagine how much more difficult this period of my life would have been had Dr. Truesdale been unwilling to generously invest his TIME and ATTENTION in me.

But as the treatments continued, so did my life. I'm proud, though still amazed, to be able to say that from March 1999 until November 2000, though the flare-ups rarely subsided, I never missed one day of work or conceded one significant life event to IBD. I recognize that I was one of the fortunate ones. Every scheduled speaking engagement (more than 150 during the period), every meeting, every family celebration, every Sunday School class, every social get-together—I was there. I may not have been in tip-top shape for each of them, but I was there.

I was determined not to let this disease adversely affect my business or the quality of life for my family. It would have devastated me to think that my wife or children would have had to miss something important or pleasurable simply because "Daddy's got this problem."

So, I labored on. And I continued to plan. When I was to be away from home, I rarely ate or drank, and when it did become necessary, only sparingly. When out in public, I always went to great pains (literally and figuratively) to locate the available restrooms well in advance of my actually needing them. When driving, I stopped at virtually every available rest area, not knowing for sure how far the next one might be.

When participating in business lunches/dinners, I would peel off and make a quick restroom stop before joining my party at our table. If the meal stretched longer than I could endure, I learned to concoct plausible excuses to disguise additional trips to the john.

For example, "Sorry folks, I can't seem to escape this darn cell phone. It's vibrating again," I would say as I rose from the table and feigned reaching for the phone on my belt. My frequent clandestine trips to the men's room were simply more desirable than having to offer graphic explanations, accompanied by anatomy lessons, between the salad and the entree.

Air travel was especially challenging during this period, and therefore, required additional planning. On average, I fly more than one hundred twenty-five times each year. My job requires it—and I dreaded each and every flight. But to cope, I created a series of plans.

For example, as a general rule I would simply eat nothing until I reached my final destination, sometimes fasting eight, ten, twelve hours or longer. I always tried to be one of the last to board the plane, allowing one more quick restroom stop before leaving the gate area.

Once on board, I would fight tooth and toenail for an aisle seat and then pray fervently for a short flight. Once airborne and having reached "our cruising altitude of 10,000 feet," I would unbuckle my seat belt and head immediately for the onboard lavatory before the line had a chance to form—whether I desperately needed to go or not.

One of the more valuable tricks I learned was to recognize the physical sensation associated with the aircraft as it started its descent—usually twenty-five to thirty minutes before scheduled touchdown. Then I would check my watch, make note of the time and start my last trip down the aisle to the john, just ahead of the flight attendant's predictable announcement admonishing passengers to "remain in your seats for the duration of the flight." I would, indeed, remain on my seat—a molded plastic one located in the lavatory—until approximately ten minutes before scheduled touchdown. At that time, I would unlock the door of my little on-board office and make my exit, walking past glaring attendants who loved to bark at me to retake my assigned seat.

My plans usually worked well. However, my resolve (defined as "bodily control") was severely tested during full flights (defined as "long lines of full bladders") and periods of unexpected turbulence causing me to be restricted to my seat. Prolonged holding patterns were nothing short of hellish, as seconds seemed like minutes and minutes like hours. Wave after wave of nausea and "goose bumps" would sweep over my body from head to toe—then back again. A cold, clammy sweat would appear as my body became rigid—every muscle tensed in an effort to "stem the flow." I'm sure I have flown more than 100,000 miles with my rear end drawn so tightly that, well, let's just say that a colonoscopy would have been an impossibility.

During the first twelve to fifteen months of my disease, I'm still amazed that no more than a handful of close friends knew the true extent of my condition. Susan and I didn't wish to worry others unnecessarily. As for my extended family, they were totally unaware of the difficulties I was facing daily. More than 700 miles, the distance from our adopted home in Ocala, Florida, to my native hometown of Princeton, Kentucky, separated us. However, after the second Saturday of September I could keep it a secret no longer.

On that day each year Princeton, Kentucky celebrates the annual Black Patch Festival. The festival itself commemorates the county's historical connection to and economic importance of burley tobacco for western Kentucky. It is a daylong affair that attracts several thousand people to downtown Princeton for a down-home combination of live music and lively conversation, fund raisers and funnel cakes, booths and barbecue.

I was in Princeton for the festival that year to sign copies of my then recently released book, ***You're Joe's Boy, Ain't Ya?***, a book that prominently features Princeton and many of its people. It was the first time my mother, sister, brothers and extended family members had seen me since I had been diagnosed with ulcerative colitis six months earlier. I was not a pretty sight.

I arrived in town in the midst of an extended flare-up. Everyone seemed shocked by my physical appearance. Since my last visit I had lost almost forty pounds and was down to about 160 pounds. I was gaunt and weak. My face was drawn and my eyes sunken. There was simply no disguising that I had a serious problem. I was as candid as I could be. I told them what I had and what we were doing to try to control it. My appearance was so disconcerting to them, I later learned that they were concerned that I was withholding information and that possibly my condition could ultimately be fatal. They were worried about me.

About five months later, the extent of my difficulties became even more evident to my family. My older sister, Ellen, had recently retired from her position as an elementary school teacher. Wanting to help her celebrate, I called and told her to name an appropriate retirement gift that she really wanted. To my surprise, she said, "I want to travel with you to one of your speaking engagements. I would love to see you work and it would give us an opportunity to spend some one-on-one time together."

I loved the idea. It would be the first time that just the two of us had traveled together in more than twenty-five years. I made the arrangements and soon we were together for one of my engagements in northern California.

We spent three days together, all of it in the midst of yet another of my serious flare-ups. Besides the diarrhea, I was experiencing considerable bleeding, stomach cramps and fever. It was impossible to camouflage the extent and severity of my problem. I confided in Ellen my deepest concerns that none of the treatment options were working and that, in fact, I was certain that my condition was steadily worsening. I admitted for the first time that I feared surgery might become necessary. She expressed her love and concern, assuring me that she and the entire family would always be there for me.

Through each of these long and torturous months of flare-ups and frustration, the only thing I could consistently count on for relief was the steroid, Prednisone. Though they have proven extremely effective for many IBD sufferers, the various anti-inflammatory drugs I experimented with simply were of no observable benefit for my condition. The diets I tried were little more than exercises in futility. With each passing month, I became more and more frustrated—and all the while sicker. Nothing was working. Nothing that is, except Prednisone. Prednisone was my friend, or at least I thought so.

Prednisone is an extremely effective drug for a variety of conditions. From asthma to infections, Prednisone is a drug that can be counted on to offer undeniable relief. On the various occasions that Dr. Truesdale prescribed Prednisone for me, he did so to stem the tide of a particularly acute flare-up I was experiencing. Each time it worked like a charm. Amazingly, the diarrhea would subside and my energy would return. Like clockwork, within a matter of a few days, I would feel like a new man again—reminiscent of my old, pre-IBD self.

But Prednisone was not a panacea. Lest I should forget, Dr. Truesdale was diligent in reminding me of that fact often. Once on Prednisone, one has to gradually taper off the level of usage over an extended period of time. On two different occasions, I was prescribed large doses of Prednisone (40-mg). Each time it took as much as four months or longer to gradually wean my body off it.

Dr. Truesdale was also quick to remind me that prolonged use of Prednisone can be a problem in and of itself. Prednisone is so powerful that, over time, studies have determined definitively that it can adversely affect systems within the body causing any number of problems ranging from ***osteoporosis***, to ***glaucoma***, to liver damage, to high blood pressure, to significant loss of muscle mass, and the list goes on.

That's why by the time Independence Day rolled around again—more than fifteen months after the initial diagnosis—I was looking forward to being off Prednisone once and for all. About four months earlier, Dr. Truesdale had reluctantly prescribed Prednisone "one more time" to help turn the tide of yet another flare-up. He prescribed 40-mg a day to start with. But he also recommended that I start taking various vitamin supplements, including calcium, to help replenish some of my body's nutrients he feared the Prednisone was destroying.

I could tell he was not excited about putting me back on another round of steroids. Frankly, neither was I. I had welcomed the opportunity to feel better, but I was informed enough to recognize the risks. I knew this would be my last chance with Prednisone. If it didn't work this time, I promised myself I would do something different in the future.

Independence Day found us enjoying a two-week family vacation on beautiful Kentucky Lake near our roots in western Kentucky. Longtime friends Joe and Karen Owen, had made their lake home ours for the duration of our vacation. It was an idyllic setting. Water, sun, shade, family, friends—the perfect place to relax. I was enjoying this vacation even more because my colitis had been in total remission for several weeks, thanks in part to my old friend, Prednisone. This brief period of remission would prove to be the beginning of the end of my battle with ulcerative colitis and IBD.

On July 6th I took my last 1-mg dose of Prednisone. After 126 days I was finally, once again Prednisone free. Better still, I felt terrific. A few days later our vacation ended and we returned to our home in Florida. The next nine days were great.

But on July 16th, a mere ten days following the completion of my most recent Prednisone treatment, the diarrhea and the blood returned. I was devastated. I tried to will them away. I tried to ignore the telltale symptoms of which I had become so intimately aware. I even lied to Susan, telling her I felt fine, hoping that if I said the words often enough…I feel fine…I feel fine…I feel fine…it would make it so.

It didn't.

On July 18th I could stand it no longer. I called Dr. Truesdale's office and reported my most recent flare-up to Carla. A short time later, Truesdale himself returned my call, wanting to know the details. I was certain I could hear the frustration in his voice. For months, we had battled this disease together, but to no avail. He told me he would call in a prescription for ***CORT enemas***. It was the only method of treatment he had not yet tried. He didn't sound especially hopeful.

If Truesdale was frustrated, I was forlorn. I started the enemas immediately and continued them for the next sixteen days. They offered absolutely no relief. On August 4th, I hit bottom. I had been spiraling downward for months, my condition was obviously deteriorating and my resolve was being severely tested. Yet time after time I continued to rally myself mentally, primarily through hope, positive affirmations and determination. But on this day, I realized I just couldn't take it any more.

On that day I was in Washington, D.C., for the opening of the annual convention of the National Speakers Association, to which I had belonged since 1988. The event is one I look forward to all year. It provides me an opportunity to have my professional batteries charged, while allowing me time to enjoy the company of speaker friends from all over the world. Yet this year, during the opening ceremonies, I was as sick as I had ever been—diarrhea, bleeding, cramps and severe fatigue. I was a mess. And though surrounded by friends and colleagues, I had never felt more alone.

As sick as I was physically, I was in even worse shape emotionally. For more than nineteen long months I had fought the good fight. I had struggled through pain and suffering with very few public complaints. I didn't whine to others about my troubles, because in my heart of hearts I was sure inner courage and intestinal fortitude (raw guts) would eventually win out—the guts it took to look this disease in the eye and not blink. The guts to take whatever this disease had to dish out and to keep coming back, again and again and again. I just knew I could do it. I knew I could beat this thing. Superman never gave up.

But there in a fancy hotel room in the heart of our nation's capital, I came to the stark realization that it takes more than guts. For months I had done all I could do—and yet it was never enough. Silently, desperately, in the quiet solitude of that room, I collapsed across the bed and prayed to God Almighty for strength. Strength to endure. I realized consciously for the first time that if I was to get better, I had to let go and let God lead the fight.

As I lay there praying, I began to sense a feeling of comfort and relief wash over me. Though they may have been present, I must admit I saw no angels attending to my needs. Though I felt His presence, God did not communicate audibly with me. Though my body was sick and frail, my faith remained healthy and strong. In the next few moments my direction became clear. I knew what I needed to do.

As I gathered my strength and composure, I sat up and reached for the hotel phone. I dialed Dr. Truesdale's office and asked to speak with Carla.

"Carla, this is Phillip Van Hooser. I'm calling from Washington, D.C. I'm in the midst of a flare-up again. Please set aside some time on Wednesday for me to drop by the office for a consultation with Dr. Truesdale. I've made a decision. I'm ready to do what has to be done."

5

For Better or For Worse

The balance of my time at the Washington convention was both difficult and invaluable. Difficult in that my overall health was deteriorating. I knew it. I could feel it. Invaluable because I forced myself to make a crucial decision.

Yet even with the physical problems I was experiencing somehow, down deep, once my decision was made I discovered an unknown reservoir of newfound resolve. From this reservoir I drew the necessary strength and stamina to formulate my plan. I knew what needed to be done. I began the process of planning how to do it.

As my plan began to take shape, the first step was crystal clear. Before I met with Dr. Truesdale, I needed to have a heart-to-heart talk with Susan.

Susan Van Hooser is one of the strongest and most determined women I have ever known. Beginning with a chance meeting, our relationship spans more than half of both of our lives. It has grown from casual awareness to harmless flirtation to mutual attraction to lifelong commitment. The observable results? A solid marriage, three wonderful children and a vital business partnership, to name just three. With that said, to suggest that our time together has been a cakewalk for Susan would be laughable.

Our first recorded meeting occurred during the summer before Susan's sixteenth birthday. I was already twenty-two. Our paths certainly crossed earlier than that, since we lived in the same small town of fewer than six thousand people. But prior to that summer encounter, I don't remember her. After that first meeting I never forgot her.

The scene was reminiscent of hundreds just like it during my youth. At every opportunity I would jump in the car, or join my buddies and head for the local Burger Queen. The Princeton Burger Queen was the recognized gathering place for the young people of our community. It was *the* place to see and be seen.

Few forays were actually made into the restaurant itself during the course of an evening. That's where the "establishment" (ancient individuals in their 30's and 40's) sat talking and drinking coffee for hours at a time. They were to be avoided and ignored—especially if some of them were your parents. The only good reasons to enter the establishment were to use the restroom facilities, to buy a bite to eat (my personal favorite was a double cheeseburger with tarter sauce—a specialty made to order, thus assuring freshness), or to check out which cute girls were working the counter.

Susan started working the counter when she was fourteen. On the day we met, she was already in her official brown and gold polyester uniform. It was late afternoon. Her shift would start later. The rush of humanity wouldn't hit for another two or three hours. So she took the opportunity to join a group of her friends in the parking lot for some casual conversation.

That afternoon I found myself with a little spare time on my hands. I was circling The Queen when I spotted a promising group of young ladies standing at the end of the parking lot. I didn't recognize any of them. That fact alone called for closer inspection. I parked my car and strolled over for a closer look.

"Good afternoon, ladies," I offered cheerfully, as I entered their midst. They immediately began to giggle. I glanced around and quickly realized these "young ladies" were in fact, no more than adolescent girls. Much too young for me. Worse still, there wasn't a familiar face in the bunch.

For this moment though, with nothing better to do, I decided to spend a little more time with these young fast-food debutantes. One by one, I faced each girl and introduced myself before asking her name. Most giggled nervously in the presence of an "older man." Most, but not all. Eventually, I turned my attention to the unfamiliar petite, green-eyed blonde.

"Hi, my name is..." I started, but was never given the opportunity to finish.

"I know who you are," she replied confidently. "You've been to my house."

"I have?" I had no idea what she was talking about.

"Yes, you have. About six years ago, when I was in third or fourth grade, you came to visit my brother after he had a motorcycle accident."

"Well, who is your brother?" I asked, still not making the connection.

"Jeff Alsobrook," she replied with a big smile. Jeff Alsobrook was a year younger than I and a former Caldwell County Tiger football teammate.

"So you're Jeff's sister. I didn't even know Jeff had a sister."

"Well, he does and you're looking at her," she said, still grinning.

We talked for a few more minutes. I asked her the expected questions—how old she was, what grade she was in and how long she had been working at Burger Queen. From her energetic responses to my questions I sensed she was bright and, I suspected, motivated.

"Where do you want to go to college?"

"I'll probably go to Murray State," she answered.

"What are you planning to study?"

"I plan to be an accountant."

I flippantly said, "Well, that's great. I plan to own my own business someday. When I do, I'll get you to keep my books."

"I'll look forward to it," she said with a broad smile.

I don't remember anything else in particular about that first conversation. I thought she was cute, though very young. But her confident air most favorably impressed me. She was certainly not cocky or arrogant, but she was no shrinking violet either. She struck me as being someone who would do whatever she set her mind and hand to.

Weeks after our initial meeting, I took a job 225 miles away. Over the next four years, we saw each other infrequently. Nevertheless, Susan made a point of staying in touch by way of cards, letters and an occasional phone call. Periodically, she would send me photos and written descriptions of how her life was unfolding. I literally watched her blossom into a beautiful young woman with the receipt of every new batch of snapshots.

During her junior year in college, we began a long distance courtship. Due to the three hundred miles separating us, we seldom saw each other more frequently than once every four to six weeks. Despite the distance, our relationship gradually became more serious.

Still I worried about the difference in our ages and life experiences. I honestly didn't think she was strong enough, gutsy enough or committed enough to successfully work through the various problems associated with a relationship built on separation, distance and age disparity. I even told her so. She proved me wrong.

As Susan reached the end of her college experience, she received the Outstanding Management Student award from the College of Business at Murray State University. She graduated with a variety of other honors. Just a few short weeks after she received her degree, we were married.

I immediately whisked her out of the only house in which she had ever lived—her parent's Old Kentucky Home—and moved her to Cape Girardeau, Missouri, where I was working. Once there, Susan quickly landed two jobs, one in convention services, the other in retail sales. She worked both concurrently.

Before long I became restless and dissatisfied with my position. One evening I made the suggestion to Susan that we both resign our jobs and spend the next six months or so traveling the country, working odd jobs as necessary to support ourselves. From my point of view, it was a wonderful idea for a young married couple. I was certain we were both intelligent enough, skilled enough and resourceful enough to make the situation work. To me, the idea sounded like a romantic adventure. To Susan, the idea sounded like sheer lunacy. She would have none of it. She wanted security.

So, 13 months after Susan joined me in Missouri, we were on the move again, this time to Ocala, Florida, where a new management job awaited me. Susan was less than thrilled. In just over one year's time, Susan had gone from the comfortable security of her family's sheltered existence to an uncertain future at best. I thought it was exciting. She thought I was nuts. So much for security!

Through it all she stayed strong. She coped by digging in and hanging on. All totaled she weathered two physical relocations (one across country), five job changes (hers and mine), new friends made, lost and made again, and to top it all off the discovery that baby number one was on the way.

"Enough!" you say? Not quite. Not yet.

After being in Florida for about two years, Susan and our then one-year-old son, Joe, returned to her parents' home in Kentucky for a brief vacation. While they were away, I made a decision that would change our lives forever. It would also serve to forever solidify in my mind Susan's level of toughness and commitment.

Simply put, I quit my job. I quit my job without another job to go to. I quit my job to start my own speaking business. Most importantly, I quit my job without discussing it in advance with Susan. I was totally convinced in my mind it was the right thing to do—and I did it without her prior knowledge. I will never forget the telephone call back to Kentucky that evening. It went exactly like this.

"Hello, Susan. How was your day?"

"Oh, Phil, it's been a wonderful day. Mom and I … (she went on and on). Joe has been so good and so cute, he …(she went on and on). I saw so and so today … (she went on and on). Phil, we miss you, but it sure has been fun being here …(she went on and on)."

Throughout her end of the conversation, I was patient. I knew my time was coming. And it finally did.

"Phil, I'm sorry, I haven't even asked about your day. How was it?"

"It was fine."

"Well, tell me about it. What did you do?"

"I quit my job," I replied simply.

For some reason, Susan never questioned whether I was joking or not. Apparently, she could tell I wasn't. Instead, she asked for restatement.

"You did what?"

"I quit my job," I repeated. "I'm going to start my speaking business."

There was a long, uninterrupted, uncomfortable pause on Susan's end of the line. As for me, I was determined not to say another word until I heard her next response. *Don't say anything else*, I thought.

Be patient. What she says next—her gut reaction will say a lot about how she will handle this new situation from now on. Her next response was a long time coming, but when she finally offered it, it was concise and to the point.

"Phil, I think I need to come home now," she offered resolutely.

We have laughed about that moment many times since that day. But it wasn't funny then. It was scary. How she handled the fear and uncertainty of the unexpected, and the reality that followed, speaks volumes about Susan.

Her gut reaction was not, "Phil, I'm staying here with my parents until you come to your senses." No, just the opposite. She said, "Phil, I think I need to come home now." Like it or not—her choice or not—she was ready to enter the fray.

Since that day, when people have heard this story recounted, the question of Susan is always the same. Incredulously, people ask, "Susan, were you scared?" For me, her response is priceless. She always responds, "Of course! It was an uncertain, frightening time. But I knew if anybody could do it, Phil could do it!"

How's that for a motivational speech? It was all the motivation I needed. I committed myself fully to making sure she was right! I didn't want to let her down. And guess what? Before the second anniversary of Van Hooser Associates, Inc., Susan had voluntarily resigned her management position with a temporary services company and started working with me full time, assuming among other things, financial and administrative responsibilities. Though she didn't have an accounting degree, almost twenty years after I casually spoke those introductory words to Susan on the Burger Queen parking lot, guess who was now keeping our books?

But that was then. This is now. And this is different. Very different. Dating, marrying, taking jobs, resigning jobs, moving, starting a business—those all seemed like small potatoes now. Each of those experiences, as stressful or exhilarating as they may have been, was based on personal choices we made. Conscious choices. The battle we now faced was certainly no choice of ours.

And this battle must be fought without the energy, exuberance and eternal optimism that traditionally accompany youth. Susan and I were somewhat older now. And we had responsibilities, restrictions and commitments. It's not just the two of us any longer. Now there are children, employees and creditors to consider. This battle would need to be fought side by side. I simply couldn't go it alone.

Upon returning home from my Washington trip, Susan and I sat down to face our future. Susan spoke first.

"You mentioned on the phone that you've made an important decision that we need to discuss when you got home. Well, you're home. What are you thinking?"

Everything I had decided over the past few days—every thought, every idea, every scenario—had been created and debated mentally, in my head. I had yet to actually share my thoughts with anyone. The process of choosing the right approach was somewhat disconcerting. With her question still lingering in the air, I sat in quiet deliberation, searching for just the right words. They didn't come quickly or easily, but eventually they began to take shape.

"Susan, this is hard for me. Harder than you can probably imagine. In my entire life, I've never faced a situation like this one."

"I know you're having a hard time, Phil. But let's face it, you're sick. Almost everybody gets sick sooner or later."

"That's just it. I know that people get sick and I know that people have serious problems," I said. "But I have always believed I would be the exception. I always envisioned living to be a hundred years old; then when I'm finally gone, having been one of those, about whom folks would say, 'Look at him lying there. He was never sick a day in his life.' I really believed I could make that happen if I tried hard enough. Well, now I know it's not possible for me."

"Okay, so what does that prove?" Susan asked, before immediately answering her own question. "It proves you're human. That's all. It doesn't mean you are weak. It doesn't mean you are any less a man."

I sat for several seconds thinking about her comments. The words had struck at the very heart of my problem. What would a "real man" do in this situation?

"Susan, I've decided when I see Truesdale tomorrow, I'm going to tell him I'm ready for that surgery, whatever that means."

Now Susan fell silent, staring straight ahead.

From the very start we had both known that surgery was a possibility. All the IBD literature had said so. Yet after more than a year and a half, I was still unsure as to what "surgery" meant exactly. Each reference to surgery I encountered seemed understated, somehow cloaked in mystery.

For example, the literature might read: *Most people who have IBD respond to their treatment program, including medication and nutritional planning...A small percentage of ulcerative colitis sufferers will ultimately require surgery...For patients with longstanding disease that is difficult or impossible to control with medicine, surgery is a welcomed option...Your doctor will consider surgery usually when certain conditions are met.*

Maybe I was just reading the literature wrong, but for me there seemed to be a disconnect. Why wasn't there as much descriptive information relative to the surgery option as there was to the disease and its other forms of treatment?

Then again, maybe it was my fault that I was not attuned to the surgical aspect of the equation. Maybe the information was readily available, yet I unconsciously disregarded it. I must admit, in the early days following my diagnosis, I never gave surgery a second thought. Why should I? I was convinced I would be numbered in the majority for whom such extreme measures would never be necessary. I had ultimate confidence that Dr. Truesdale would sooner or later find exactly the right treatment combination to send my disease into permanent remission. I could easily imagine myself as being the poster boy for "how to beat this disease."

But that had not happened. As the early days had given way to weeks, and weeks to months, it became ever clearer that I might be one of *"that small percentage of ulcerative colitis sufferers who ultimately requires surgery."* It was looking more and more as if mine might be one of those special cases. The one that defies the averages.

In the early months I had made a point of questioning Dr. Truesdale regarding the surgical options associated with ulcerative colitis. I wanted to know everything about the possibilities. Each time he would basically brush my question off by saying something like, "Phil, there's really no sense in talking about surgery. It won't come to that. So there's no sense in worrying about it unnecessarily. I'm sure we will be able to control this by way of treatments."

I believed him. Even more important, I believe he believed himself. He was bound and determined to help me beat this thing, so I followed his lead. Over time, I basically forgot about surgery.

However, more recently, with the obvious lack of sustained improvement in my condition, I secretly began to revisit the topic of surgery in my mind. I honestly didn't know what surgery really meant, but I remembered reading somewhere that surgery was the only sure cure for ulcerative colitis. But what kind of surgery? I needed to find out.

Even more telling was Truesdale's attitude these days. I was sure I was hearing slightly more resignation in his voice. His demeanor seemed less upbeat than before. With every disappointing update I offered, with every new flare-up, Truesdale seemed to struggle to reach deeper and deeper into his medical hat, never quite being able to produce the rabbit he desired. He was doing all he could, as was I. But nothing was clicking. Nothing except Prednisone, and that simply wasn't a viable long-term option.

When I began mentioning surgery again after more than a year of silence on the matter, I sensed a perceptible change in Dr. Truesdale's position. Instead of discounting my questions, he began sharing more information—not for my case necessarily, he stressed—just general information about available surgical options. During periods of casual conversation he would mention some new surgical procedure and its corresponding benefits.

On more than one occasion, Dr. Truesdale mentioned a couple of his other patients who had recently required intestinal surgery due to conditions similar, though more severe than mine. He never disclosed their names or the specifics of their cases. He just talked in basic generalities.

But he was beginning to talk freely about a topic that, for months, had seemed taboo. I even remember his saying on one occasion that one of his patients who had required surgery was doing well and if I ever wanted to talk to her, he could probably arrange it.

These and many other thoughts and observations had joined themselves together and led me to the conclusion that surgery was a logical course of action to consider. Now, after sharing my thoughts with Susan I waited for her response, hoping she would understand. After a period of careful deliberation, she looked up and spoke.

"Phil, I completely agree. I think you've reached a point that requires us to seriously consider surgery as an option. Honestly, I think you've been at that point for a while now. But it was obvious to me you weren't ready to concede. So I haven't said anything."

I was glad we were of one accord. But there was more.

"Susan, one of the main reasons I haven't done anything before this has nothing to do with me. I've gotten to the point that I'm desperate to feel better. But now I'm worried about you and the kids."

“What specifically are you worried about, Phil?”

“I’m worried that something might go wrong during the surgery and…well, it wouldn’t be fair for you to have to raise three kids alone.”

“Do what?” she asked with an intentionally exaggerated tone of sarcasm, while forcing her voice to ascend several octaves. A smile crossed her face as she looked directly at me. “Phil, I’ve been raising these kids by myself for years already. You’re gone all the time, remember?” She finished with a chuckle as she shook her head.

I know exactly what she’s doing. She wants me to be practical. This is a serious situation and we both know it. But, she thinks I’m taking myself too seriously. She’s right. I am. Since the kids have been born, my work has caused me to travel at least forty to fifty percent of the time. She has proven over and over that she’s more than capable of handling the kids, the household and a whole lot more. She’s already doing it.

Suddenly, the smile left Susan’s face. Her countenance became more serious. With her eyes fixed on mine, she reached across the table and gently placed her hand on top of mine. She then told me what I needed to hear.

“Phil, I will take you any way I can get you. Remember our promise to each other? For better or for worse. So will the kids. We love you. And because we love you, we want what’s best for you.

“It hurts me to watch you suffer the way you have been. Now if there’s no alternative to the suffering, so be it. I’ll be here for you. But we both believe that some sort of surgical procedure may help you. I think you owe it to yourself—not to us—to see if there’s anything you can do to get yourself better. I’ll tell you right now, you can count on me to be with you every step of the way. But then again, I’ll be here for you no matter what happens. Now quit worrying about us and go see what Dr. Truesdale can do to help you.”

6

Let's Rock and Roll

Susan's heartfelt words of affirmation, support and love were just what the doctor ordered. I immediately felt a mental burden evaporate. Susan was with me—completely. A surge of confidence swelled up deep in my soul.

This is the right thing to do and now is the right time to do it! I was convinced.

The next day, as I prepared for my appointment with Dr. Truesdale, I discovered yet another feeling. This one surprised me. The sensation was one of anxiousness. But not the anxious feeling that often accompanies nervousness and dread. That would have been more natural. Instead, excitement and anticipation better described my current anxious state.

In a strange way I felt as if I were standing in line to ride the "world's fastest roller coaster." As I stood, eyeing the challenge before me, butterflies formed in the hollow of my gut. I was making preparations to climb aboard, yet remained somewhat hesitant to do so. In my mind I longed for that glorious moment that arrives after the peaks and valleys of the experience have passed. The moment that comes after the fear and trepidation have dissipated. That moment at the conclusion of the ride when, safely back in the station, one can shout with exhilaration, "IT'S OVER! I DID IT—AND YES, I'D DO IT AGAIN!"

A thousand unformed thoughts flitted through my consciousness. Yet through the haze of uncertainty I was absolutely certain I was in for the ride of my life. I had nothing more to do but climb aboard. For the first time in a long time, I found myself focusing on newfound hope instead of hurt, on possibility instead of pain.

As I entered the office, Truesdale's staff responded immediately. No need to complete long, drawn out forms in triplicate this time. Instead, I was greeted warmly and personally.

"Good morning, Mr. Van Hooser."

Over the last several months I had attained a level of familiarity within this office to which I had never aspired. Like it or not, I had acquired a status similar to that of the character "Norm" on the old *Cheers* television series. Instead of a barstool I occupied an examination room table. Like Norm, when I entered the establishment, greetings echoed from every corner of the room. I had found a gastroenterologist's office where everybody knows my name.

Soon Truesdale's assistant, Carla, appeared from behind the closed door as I had seen her do so many times before. And like each time before, her words were preceded by a warm smile.

"Good morning, Mr. Van Hooser."

During the period of these many months, I had failed miserably at getting Carla to call me by my first name. Her professionalism simply wouldn't allow it.

"Morning, Carla," I responded.

"So, how are you feeling today?" she asked as she registered my current weight before ushering me into the privacy of the examination room.

"Carla, I'm tempted to tell you I'm doing fine, but if I did, I'd be lying. I've got another major flare-up under way. On top of that, I'm just really tired of this whole thing. Now how's that for being depressingly honest?" I answered, with a slight chuckle.

"I know it's been a long fight. You've had a really tough time of it," she offered with compassion as she secured the blood pressure cuff around my upper left arm.

"Yeah, I have," I admitted. "But I'm beginning to feel better about things."

"Really? Why's that?" she asked, stethoscope in her ears, eyes fixed on the cuff's pressure gauge.

"Well, I've finally made a tough decision," I said, without specifically revealing what it was. "That's what I'm here to talk to the doctor about."

My words caused Carla to steal a quick glance at my face. Had I thought about it beforehand, I would have half expected to see a look of puzzlement in her features—curiosity about my "decision." But no such look was noticeable. Carla never asked for clarification and I never offered any. But I now believe she knew and understood my unspoken decision in some ways better than I did. Maybe it had just been a matter of time all along until we finally arrived at this point.

Whatever the case, she recorded the pressure reading, stood and said, "Mr. Van Hooser, I know whatever you decide will work out well. I'll send Dr. Truesdale right in. Good luck." Her warmth and smile lingered in the air even as the door closed behind her.

And as each time before, my wait for the doctor was a brief one.

"Phil, it's good to see you," Dr. Truesdale said as he breezed into the room. We shook hands. "How are you feeling?"

As I responded, Truesdale eased into a chair across from me and crossed his legs. He leaned forward slightly and with intertwined fingers, wrapped his hands around his knee. His eyes were fixed solidly on my face. His body language spoke of total concentration. In that moment, like so many before, he made me feel as if I were his only patient—his only concern.

"I'm not feeling very good. As a matter of fact, I'm not feeling good at all. This flare-up is a bad one," I said flatly, with no emotion. I paused, took a deep breath and then continued. "But, believe it or not, I'm sort of glad this one is happening."

"Really? Why do you say that?"

"Well, this one has helped me decide the time has come for me to give serious consideration to the next step. Doc, I'm here to discuss surgery."

I tried hard to read Truesdale's face as my words registered with him. He didn't seem shocked by my revelation. But I saw no indication of relief or support in his demeanor either.

"Phil, I sense your frustration. We both know that the medical treatments we've tried so far simply haven't worked like we hoped they would. But before we talk about surgery, you need to understand there is traditionally another treatment step between where you are now and what you are considering. I need to tell you that step is immuno-suppressive medication."

Without invitation or encouragement by me, Dr. Truesdale launched into a theoretical overview related to the intent behind immuno-suppressive treatments. He carefully explained that no one knows for sure, but many medical experts believe ulcerative colitis is directly related to an overactive immune system gone awry.

As every seventh grade health student knows, the healthy human body's immune system is a wonderful thing. We have been marvelously created with our own built-in anatomical defenses. On those regular occasions when our bodies are exposed to outside germs and infections, the immune system springs to action in our defense, working to neutralize outside agents and keep them from causing life-threatening situations. For example, because of the work of a healthy immune system, a common cold rarely results in pneumonia. A paper cut seldom progresses to a potentially fatal case of gangrene.

For some unknown reason, things do occasionally go wrong. The immune system becomes misdirected. In the case of ulcerative colitis, some medical experts believe the immune system ends up attacking the colon instead of protecting it. The manifestations of these intestinal battles—the internal wounds—were exactly the type of problems I had been experiencing for months.

The immuno-suppressive theory holds that by using powerful medication to suppress the immune system's natural response mode, the internal attacks on the colon will eventually subside, allowing the problem to be controlled, or at least managed.

The argument made good sense, both when Truesdale offered it and on those numerous prior occasions when I had encountered immuno-suppressive information during my continuing research. I had read. I had studied. I understood the concept. Still, I had concerns.

My first concern had to do with very practical considerations. In my work, I shake hands with potentially hundreds of people every week. I never know what kinds of germs or infections they might be carrying.

On top of that I travel by air several times each month. Whether I like it or not, I breathe recycled air which has exited the lungs of hundreds of strangers—some healthy, some not—from every corner of the globe. Common sense tells me that, because of my lifestyle, I am already at a higher risk for possible infections than the "average" patient is. Frankly, I just didn't like the thought of having both greater risk exposure *and* a dulled immune system.

My other concern had to do with the level of predictable success of immuno-suppressive medications. I learned that many people are helped tremendously by this method of treatment. However there are no guarantees that remission will be the end result for everyone. The fact is, it takes several months of immuno-suppressive medication before even the initial effects of the treatment can be determined. In the meantime, for patients like myself who experience on-going flare-ups, the only available treatment involves continuing the use of high-dose steroids.

I explained these concerns to Truesdale with controlled emotion. I was definitive, but not defiant. For the better part of a year and a half I had listened, I had learned and I had followed my physician's instructions to the letter. Because I believed in Dr. Truesdale and because I wanted so desperately to get well, I had molded myself into the "model patient."

However now I had reached a different point in my journey. I was at a point where I felt I needed to assert myself regarding my future treatments.

I am confident Truesdale recognized this was not a knee-jerk reaction to a vulnerable moment of pain or frustration. I had done my homework and he knew it. My concerns were legitimate and served as a solid foundation for making informed decisions. I felt the time had come for me to learn more about the available surgical options. My intent was to gently nudge Truesdale in that direction. To my satisfaction, he accommodated me.

"Phil, you seem intent on exploring the surgical route. Before you make up your mind, I want you to understand exactly what such a surgery entails and the impact it will most certainly have on the rest of your life."

Dr. Truesdale stood and walked across the room to a medical poster hanging on the wall. The poster depicted a person's intestines in living color, with each important section and organ clearly labeled. He began this one-on-one anatomy lesson by pointing out the large intestine—the colon.

"Phil, the most common surgery for those who suffer from severe ulcerative colitis involves a total ***proctocolectomy***. In layman's terms, that means a surgeon removes your entire colon and rectum while salvaging your anal muscles. Let me explain exactly how it all works.

"The food and drink we ingest make their way to the stomach and, with the help of appropriate stomach acids, are broken down primarily into a liquid state. This liquid solution then leaves the stomach through a passage known as the ***duodenum*** and travels through the ***jejunum*** and into the ***ileum***. These three sections make up the small intestine.

"The small intestine is a rather small gauge organ, approximately twelve to fifteen feet in length, which winds back and forth through the abdominal cavity. While in the small intestine, almost all the ***nutrients*** the body needs from the food are absorbed through the intestinal walls, directly entering the blood stream. Eventually, all the unnecessary 'leftovers' from the digestive process leave the ileum by way of the ***ileocecal valve*** and are deposited into the colon."

Dr. Truesdale stole a quick glance over his shoulder at me. Certain he had my full attention he continued his "show-and-tell" demonstration.

"The colon is the body's primary physical waste removal system. It provides two important services—***absorption*** and storage. The waste that enters the colon from the ileum is approximately ninety-eight percent liquid. In a healthy colon the vast majority of the liquid is absorbed before the body deposits the remaining waste elsewhere. This liquid is absorbed directly through the lining of the colon, returning it to the bloodstream, where it is used to re-hydrate the body.

"This process occurs as the waste is gradually pushed, by way of muscular contractions, upward through the ascending colon, across through the transverse colon, down through the descending colon and eventually, through the sigmoid colon. After it has traveled through the sigmoid colon, this now near-solid residue is stored in the rectum, located just above the ***anal canal***, until it becomes convenient for the carrier (you or me) to rid ourselves of it. We do so during convenient trips to the toilet.

"When you think about it, this is an amazingly efficient system that works extremely well in most people. Unfortunately, Phil, you happen to be one of the exceptions. Any questions yet?"

As I followed Truesdale's explanation, I found myself focusing on the picture of the organ he identified as the colon. It was not unfamiliar to me. I had seen it pictured in dozens of science books and magazines. Growing up on a farm, I had physically handled the intestines of butchered animals many times before. Of course, I had become even more familiar with the workings of the colon since being diagnosed with IBD. Still, prior to this moment, I realized I had never really given much thought to the physical dimensions of the colon itself.

"Yeah, I've got a question. How big is the colon anyway?" I asked.

Dr. Truesdale answered. "The average person's colon is four to six feet in length. Its diameter is considerably bigger than a vacuum cleaner hose and it is pliable. It easily expands and contracts depending on the volume of its contents."

While still looking at the poster of "intestinal man," I tried to imagine the hollow void in the abdominal cavity once the colon had been removed. The thought unnerved me slightly as I recalled the many butchered animals I had seen over the years. But I kept these thoughts to myself and offered no additional questions. Truesdale continued.

"Once the colon and rectum have been removed, the attending surgeon takes the lower section of the small intestine—the ileum—and carefully cuts and splices until he is able to construct a ***reservoir***, or ***pouch***, that will serve as a new rectum. Once constructed, the pouch then is attached directly to the ***anus muscles*** and anal canal.

"For all intents and purposes, at this point in the surgery, everything is anatomically where it needs to be. But because of the trauma involved with the cutting and splicing, this newly created pouch needs time to heal and rest before it is put into service. So the surgeon creates a '***temporary loop ileostomy***' above the newly created pouch."

"Okay, hold it right there," I interrupted. "That's a new one to me. What is it?"

"In essence, an incision is made in the lower abdomen. The surgeon then goes through that incision and retrieves a section of the ileum above the new pouch and pulls that loop of intestine to the surface of the outer wall of the abdomen. The surgeon then attaches the intestine securely to the abdominal wall and creates a small opening in the exposed loop.

"For the next ninety days or so, the individual will wear an external ***ostomy appliance*** (commonly referred to as a ***bag***) that will capture all the waste that flows through the ileum *before* it reaches the pouch. This three-month period of inactivity allows for complete healing of the newly created pouch.

He makes it sound so easy, so natural. But it's not natural. And it won't be easy for me.

"Once the appropriate healing period has passed, a much simpler surgical procedure is used to close the loop ileostomy. In essence the new plumbing is reconnected, allowing waste to flow through the ileum and into the pouch, where it is stored before it is deposited outside of the body. This second surgery traditionally requires a much shorter recovery period.

"Phil, that is the scope of the surgery in a nutshell. Afterward, with the exception of a few lifestyle changes, almost everything will be back to normal for you."

For a long moment I sat quietly digesting Truesdale's comments. He had been efficient with his words, carefully avoiding most of the incoherent "doctor talk" usually associated with technical medical explanations. He recognized how important it was that I understood clearly what he was saying.

And understand I did. I understood to the point of personal discomfort. It wasn't so much the explanation of the surgery that bothered me. More specifically, it was the short-term result he had described. The very thought of wearing a bag made me cringe.

This was not the first time I had ever heard of people wearing—what did he call them? Ostomy appliances? This was the first time, however, that I had ever considered the possibility that *I* might have to wear one.

I quickly searched my memory bank for occasions, over the years, when the subject of an individual with an "external appliance" had arisen. I was sure I had never known anyone personally who had worn one. However there were vague recollections of faceless, unnamed individuals who, at different times, had been pointed out to me. These folks always seemed to be very old or very sick. One thing I did remember clearly. In each instance, the person "wearing a bag" seemed to be whispered about in depressing, muted tones.

As I recall, such conversations would be brief and one-sided. Additional, follow-up questions never seemed appropriate or necessary. The fact that an appliance had to be worn was information enough.

The whispers usually went something like this: "Phil, see that lady over there? She has to wear a bag, bless her heart," or "Mr. Jones is in such bad shape, he's got a permanent bag. It's so sad. It's just pitiful."

I never remember any consideration being given to the possibility that "wearing a bag" might actually be an improvement in the quality of life for the wearer. I certainly never remember it being seen as having its own advantages. The peering eyes and piercing words were always focused on the negative—on the bag.

I have learned that ignorance is the absence of information or knowledge, sometimes both. Unfortunately, I've also learned that ignorance is not always bliss. Too often, from ignorance grows pity, disgust or fear. My ignorance of external appliances brought forth all three.

Pity...*Is this the first step toward my becoming old and sick? Am I already too sick to get better, but nobody has had the courage to tell me? Will this ruin my life?*

Disgust...*How can anyone adapt to such a situation? Intestinal waste draining into a bag hanging from my side? I'm a young man. How will I ever be able to go out in public again? Is this what I have to look forward to for the next forty or fifty years?*

Fear...*Will I ever be able to be intimate with my wife again? Will I be able to continue to travel and speak? Will my children just see me as a pitiful old man?*

As these and other thoughts entered my mind, I began to feel my former optimism sag and fade. I came to this appointment with a determination to use surgery as my means of getting better. Now, in my mind, my situation had worsened.

Suddenly I realized while I sat engaged in my own personal pity party, I also sat in full view of Truesdale's measured gaze. I realized he was reading my reaction to his description of the surgery. I became even more uncomfortable. I needed to regain a measure of emotional control. Quickly, I created a diversion—an emotional smoke screen—in an effort to disguise my primary concern.

"Uhm, what kind of lifestyle changes?" I asked feebly.

Truesdale dutifully answered.

"Phil, for the most part, the changes in your lifestyle should be fairly minor. For example, after the proper healing period, you will be able to engage in virtually any activity that you choose. You will be able to participate in sports and other activities requiring various levels of physical exertion. You will be able to eat almost anything you want. There may be isolated exceptions, but those will be determined by experimentation over time."

"Okay, what else then? Are there any other problems I should be aware of?"

"Well, it's certain that you will have to make more frequent trips to the rest room than an average person. Your new pouch simply won't have the same volume capacity that your colon does."

"How many trips? Give me an estimate."

"Again, it's hard to say for sure. People are different. Some will have to go more often than others. The experts often say six trips a day is average and possibly once during the nighttime hours. Big eaters will obviously go more often. But the good thing is you won't have the urgency you have now. You will be able to 'hold it' much longer than your condition presently allows."

To the average person who had never suffered the ill effects of IBD, six or seven trips a day to the john might seem excessive, even burdensome. To me, *only* six or seven trips a day sounded like heaven.

This question and answer period had both given me relevant information *and* bought me sufficient time to regroup emotionally. It was now time to work my way back to my most troublesome concern—the "appliance" issue. I was desperate to know more.

"Uhm, about this bag, er, I mean appliance. How can you be certain it will only be temporary?"

"Phil, I'm going to tell you straight out there are no absolute promises. Lots of things can happen once the surgical team gets inside and starts looking around. But I can tell you this. Twenty years or so ago this surgery was not possible. Then no one had learned how to use the ileum to create the pouch I've just described to you. In those days an ileostomy was *always* permanent. I know how frightening this all must sound to you. But medical science has come a long way and you are one of the lucky ones."

"Lucky? Doc, I'll be honest. I don't feel very lucky right now."

"Phil, listen carefully to me. You *are* one of the lucky ones for a number of reasons. First, other than your problem with IBD, you are in wonderful physical health. The fact that you are young, strong and fit is a tremendous advantage at this point. As difficult as this type of surgery is, I see no reason why you won't be able to tolerate it well.

"Secondly, your positive mental attitude, to this point, has been remarkable. Most casual observers don't realize that IBD is not just a physical ailment. Over time, IBD has a way of working on a person's psychological and emotional well being, too. Believe me when I tell you I have seen IBD patients who basically resign themselves to a life of misery. But not you. You have fought through every setback. You haven't given up. Phil, your will and determination may be your greatest asset.

"Most importantly, you *are* one of the lucky ones because you can be *cured*! But to be cured, you have to give up your colon. Think about it, Phil. No colon, no colitis. Of course, no colitis means no more cramps and no more bleeding. No more desperate dashes to the nearest toilet—twelve, fifteen, twenty or more times a day.

"Phil, I'm sure right now the thought of an ***ileostomy***, even a temporary one, to a young, active person like yourself, if not frightening, is at least unsettling. Nobody wants to have one. But in this case it is the only way for you to get better. And based on the history of your condition, this surgery is bound to be necessary for you sooner or later. I really believe it's better to have the surgery as a healthy 40-something, than to suffer for another ten or fifteen years with IBD and then hope for a successful surgery at fifty or sixty years of age."

Truesdale's straightforward comments hit their intended mark. They struck both at my emotional state and at my sensibility.

I'm not the only person who has ever been through this. And Truesdale's right. I've met every challenge so far and have gotten through each one. My faith, my family and my physician have been with me throughout. I can't give up at this point. I won't give up now.

"Doc, I have to admit, the thought of a bag bothers me a little."

There it was. Truesdale had finally discovered my greatest concern. I had reached a point that there wasn't much need in trying to hide it any longer.

"And you're right, I am lucky. I'm lucky to be healthy. I'm lucky to have Susan in my corner. And I'm lucky to have you helping me through the tough spots. If this is what it will take for me to get better, then I'm not going to quit now."

I now believe that honest, observable concern is exactly what Dr. Truesdale had wanted to see all along. He needed to know that I was deeply concerned before he felt comfortable in recommending such a dire course of action and before I made any hasty, ill-informed decisions.

From past experience Truesdale knew that courage and bravado alone would not be enough to get me through this stage of the battle. He wanted me to be concerned enough to do the necessary homework. He wanted me to be concerned enough to hold strong to this life-changing decision, especially after the emotion in which it was made had worn away.

"Phil, I'm glad to hear that. This is a huge decision, but I assure you there are some really talented, highly skilled surgeons out there who can do amazing things. They help a lot of people. I believe they can help you."

By this time, my physician's back was turned completely to his visual aid. It had served its purpose well. He faced me directly, staring deep into my eyes.

"Phil, I can't emphasize enough how critical your decision is regarding this type of surgery. This is major surgery," he said, over emphasizing the word "major." "Surgery such as this should never be considered casually. You will be off work completely for two or three months with the first surgery and for a month or more with the reversal. The possibility of complications always exists. Do you clearly understand all this?"

"Yeah, I think I do," I said.

"Well, then, I've got an important question for you. With all this information, why do you want this surgery?"

Truesdale's question was a good one. In spite of the graphic surgical description he offered and the concerns it evoked for me personally, I still knew the answer.

"Doc, my reason for considering this surgery is fairly simple. I can't imagine continuing to live like I am now if any other options are available. Right now, the quality of my life stinks. I'm in near constant pain. My energy level has never been lower. The lion's share of my thoughts center around when my next mad dash to a toilet will be. And with each passing month the problem seems to get worse."

"Every aspect of who I am has suffered under the weight of this disease. I am not the husband, father, friend or professional that I used to be and that I want to be again. I am ready to do something to bring this situation under control. I know that Prednisone is not the answer for me. I am simply not willing to gamble with the long-term risks. You've been honest with me up until now. So here's my question for you. Can the surgery you've described help me or not?"

Dr. Truesdale paused before answering. He continued to look directly into my eyes.

"Yes, Phil, I think surgery can help you. I had hoped it wouldn't come to this. Honestly, in the early days I never thought it would. But now there is no question in my mind that you have become steroid dependent and our long term treatment options are very limited."

"Steroid dependent? What exactly does that mean?" I asked

uneasily.

"Phil, relax," Truesdale said, immediately sensing my concern. "Being 'steroid dependent' doesn't mean you're addicted to steroids. The term simply means that we have been able to determine through trial and error, that nothing else works to control your condition except steroids. And another thing. We are in complete agreement that at your age, at your stage of life, the risk of additional medical complications is simply too great to leave you on steroids indefinitely."

Truesdale paused and thought briefly before continuing.

"Now, in a perfect world I would have liked to experiment with the immuno-suppressive treatments. However, in light of the concerns you've expressed, coupled with the uncertain results we can anticipate from them, I feel the time is right to refer you to a surgeon for further consultation."

Truesdale's candor was refreshing. My confidence in him was such that I believed if he thought surgery could help me, I was certain it could. Even the thought of wearing an appliance would not dissuade me.

"Well, what's the next step then?" I asked.

"If you're ready, we need to identify a reputable surgical group who specializes in this procedure and have you consult with them."

"I'm ready. Who do you recommend?"

"Phil, there are a number of excellent surgeons in this area who are trained to conduct this type of surgery. But I've got to tell you that this type of surgery is not their main focus. In fact, they may only operate on patients like you a few times each year. I would feel better referring you to a group that conducts this type of surgery dozens, even hundreds, of times each year."

"Who do you have in mind?"

"There are a number of reputable institutions that specialize in this surgical discipline around the country. One of the premier institutions and the one I recommend you consider is the Cleveland Clinic in Cleveland, Ohio. Are you familiar with it?"

"Honestly, no," I responded.

"Well, I suggest it for two reasons. First, it is without question, one of the finest medical facilities in the United States, if not the entire world. People come from all over the globe to be treated there. Secondly, unlike many of my patients who prefer to be treated close to home, your job requires you to travel so much already. So I didn't think it would bother you as much to travel elsewhere for treatment."

"Doc, I definitely want to go where they know what they're doing. I'm fairly familiar with Cleveland, Ohio. Over the years I've given several presentations there. As a matter of fact, I have a couple of clients in that area that I'm working with now. But I'm not familiar with the Cleveland Clinic. So before I make any final decisions about what I will or won't do, I would like to take a scouting trip up there to meet the surgeons and see the facilities. Can you arrange that?"

Truesdale nodded.

"I believe we can handle that. I'll have someone call this afternoon and see when the Clinic would be available to have you come for a consultation. Then you can check your schedule and confirm the appointment. How does that sound?"

"It sounds like we have turned the corner and are headed in a new direction," I said.

Truesdale began the process of furiously scribbling notes to go in my file. He spoke as he wrote.

"Let's see, it's almost the middle of August now. By the time you go up for this appointment, the humidity shouldn't be as bad there as it is here in Florida. If you can, you ought to have dinner at one of those great outdoor restaurants around the inner harbor of Lake Erie and then maybe catch a Cleveland Indians baseball game. Or, come to think of it, you could always visit the new *Rock and Roll Hall of Fame* they've built downtown. I hear it is really nice..."

As Truesdale continued the trivial conversation that was certainly intended to lighten my mood, I couldn't help but think: *That's just perfect. I'll be flying a thousand miles to discuss the life-changing process of surrendering my colon, while thousands of revelers congregate in Cleveland to eat, drink and be merry, watch baseball and celebrate the musical accomplishments of their idols—Elvis, Chuck Berry, The Beatles and more. Oh, well, if you can't beat 'em, join 'em.*

Let's rock and roll!

This picture was taken two weeks after I was diagnosed with ulcerative colitis. I had already lost about twenty-five pounds. (March 1999)

My brother, Mark, and I during our hometown's Black Patch Festival. I was in the midst of a major flare-up, but few people knew. My weight had dropped more than thirty pounds. (September 1999)

With dear friends, Anna Jo Wyman and Anthony Stallins at our 25th high school reunion. I had just decided to go through with the procotcolectomy and J-pouch surgery. My face was full and puffy from high doses of prednisone. (September 2000)

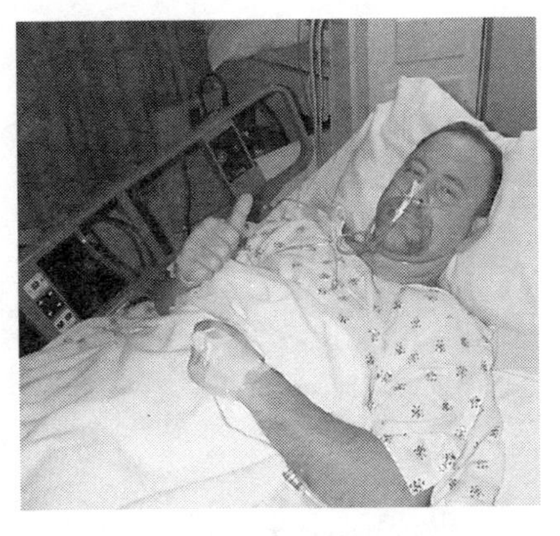

This was taken a few hours after my initial surgery. Was I giving a positive "thumbs up" or thumbing for a ride back to Florida? (November 10, 2000)

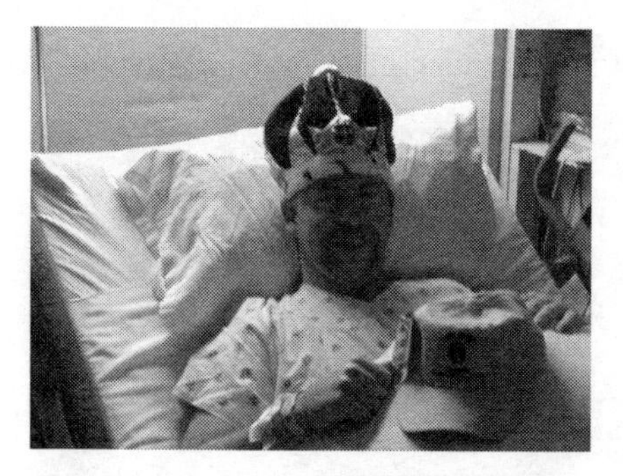

To lift my spirits, my siblings presented me my own crown and named me "king for a day." (November 2000)

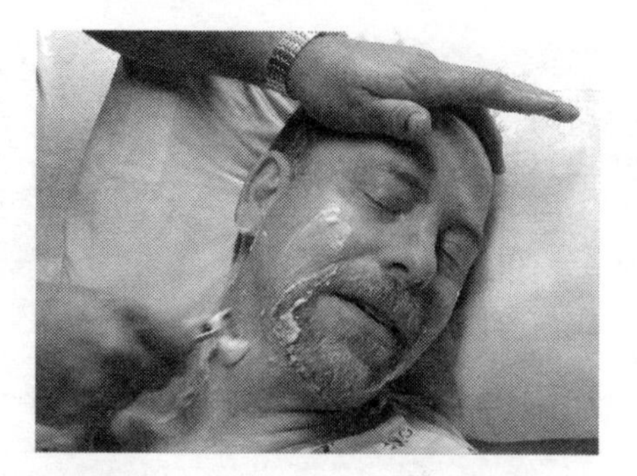

Mark kept me occupied by giving me a shave. I was brave to give him a razor! (November 2000)

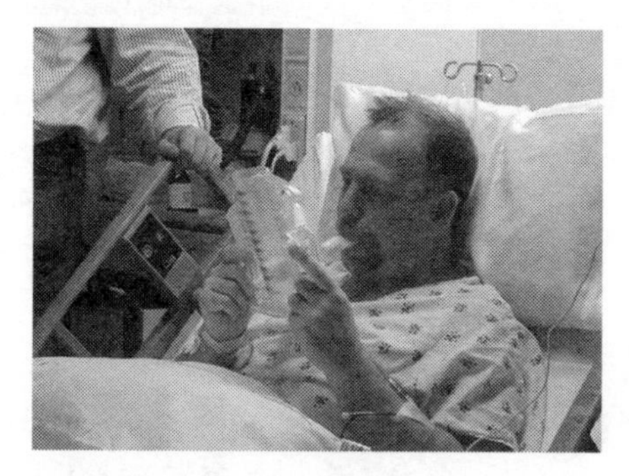

My brother, Dan, oversaw my spirometry treatments. (November 2000)

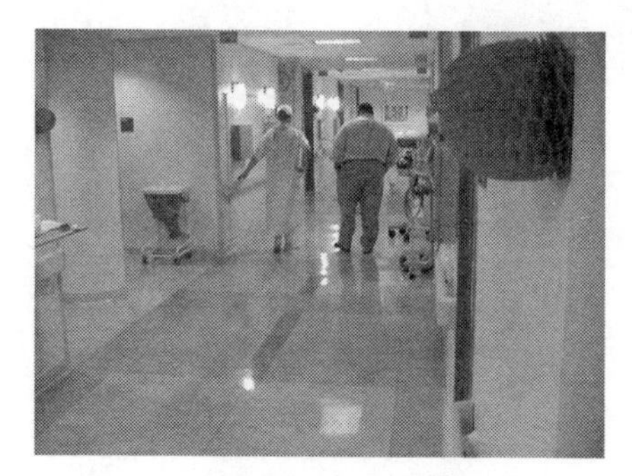

I spent a lot of time shuffling through the halls of the Cleveland Clinic. This trip, I was accompanied by my buddy, Jim McDaniel. (November 2000)

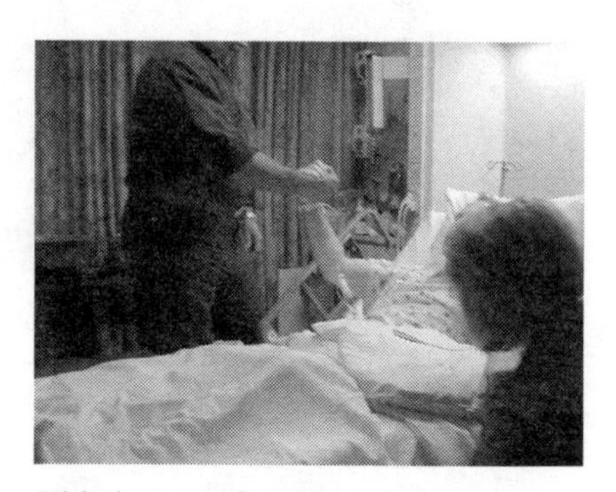

This is one of my favorite photos for its symbolism. Someone was always reaching out to me during my time of need. (November 2000)

I returned to Cleveland optimistic about my reconnection surgery. I am celebrating my last night with an ileostomy with Mark, Ellen and Dan. (February 22, 2001)

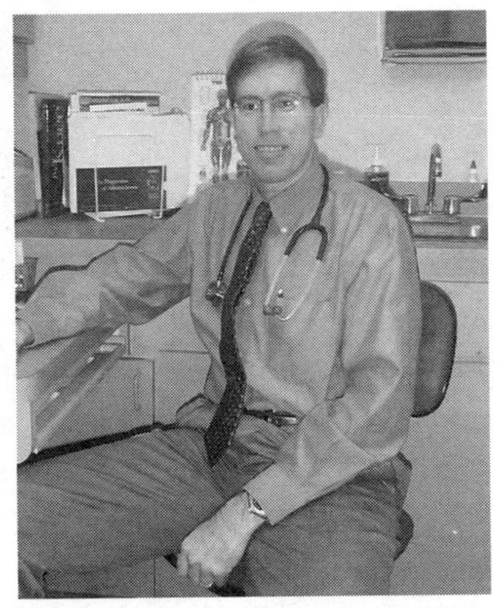

Throughout my two-year struggle with IBD, I received great support from my Florida healthcare support group. Dr. Glen Morgan, my primary care doctor.

My gastroenterologist, Dr. Richard Truesdale and his assistant, Carla Zimmerman. This team gave me exceptional care and support, both medically and emotionally.

A survivor of IBD, I enjoy a full and active life. My wife, Susan, and I enjoyed a few days on the slopes of our favorite ski town, Steamboat Springs, CO! (December 2001)

I am healthy again! Now I am volunteering my efforts with the Crohn's and Colitis Foundation of America to help find a cure for IBD. I am pictured with Rodger DeRose, CEO of the Crohn's and Colitis Foundation of America. (November 2002)

Here I am speaking at the first "IBD Advocacy Day" event in Washington, DC. (June 2003)

My family is my inspiration for finding a cure for IBD. From left, Sophie, Sarah, Joe, Susan, and me. (August 2003)

Here I am introducing Senator Harry Reid, D-Nevada, at the "IBD Advocacy Day" event. Senator Reid sponsored legislation to support funding for continued IBD research. (June 2003)

7

How Can I Help You?

Dr. Truesdale was a man of his word. The day after our appointment, I received a call from Cleveland, Ohio. A few minutes later I had written in ink, on my personal calendar the following:

September 14, 2000, 1:00 p.m.
Cleveland Clinic, Cleveland, OH
Colorectal Surgery Department—Dr. Ian Lavery
"Scouting Trip"

One long distance telephone call and a few strokes of a pen and—voila—a new direction for my life had been set in motion. With this singular commitment my mind sprang into action. I began to think about all the things that I needed to do and all the plans that Susan and I needed to make.

Let's see, the first thing I need to do is see if I can find a cheap flight to Cleveland. It's just over four weeks to the date of the appointment, so I should be able to get a discount from some airline. I won't need to stay overnight. I'll just fly up that morning and back that evening. I'm sure Susan will want to go along, but I'll try to talk her out of it. There's really no sense in her going. That would just be additional expense for a plane ticket. If this surgery is going to require me to be off work for several weeks, we need to start watching our pennies now. I'll be sure to take good notes and fill her in on all that I learned when I get back.

Now what should we do about Joe, Sarah and Sophie? For the last several months they've seen their daddy spending a lot of time in the bathroom, yet I seriously doubt that any of the three have figured out that something was terribly wrong. On the other hand, they are sharp kids. At thirteen, eleven and five, I'm sure they know more than I think they know. Still, I don't want to do or say anything that will frighten them unnecessarily. It will probably be best to just not tell them anything about the surgery until my plans are more concrete. They will just think my trip to Cleveland is another speaking engagement. I'll be sure to sit down and talk to them as soon as I get back.

What about our friends? What's the best way to break the news to them? Only a handful of them even know that I have a problem. But I'm sure none of them have any idea that surgery is looming on the horizon.

Maybe I've been wrong in not sharing more information with my extended family members—Mom, Ellen, Mark and Dan—before now. But Mom would have been worried sick. As for Ellen, the surgery probably won't come as a big surprise. After all, she witnessed first hand how sick I was when we traveled to California together a few months ago. Mark and Dan may be a different story. Brothers aren't supposed to keep secrets from one another. But I have.

Well, it's too late to worry about all that now. I just wonder how they will react to the news? I sure don't want anybody feeling sorry for me. That's the last thing I need.

The thing that worries me most right now is work. Truesdale said the average person would have to be off work for about two months following the first surgery and another month or so after the reversal. I can't afford to be off work that long. I'll bet he's just exaggerating. If the average is two months, I can probably be back to work in one. Still, before I go to Cleveland for my consultation, I'd better check my speaking calendar for a slow period so the business impact won't be as great.

These and dozens of other thoughts and issues crossed my mind during that day and the days that followed. I constantly mulled over various actions that needed to be taken while determining others that could wait. The thought of my upcoming surgery was never far from the forefront of my mind. But it was rarely the thought of the surgery itself that I considered. Rather, I was thinking about the practical implications the surgery would have.

Though many of the actions I considered were worthy of delay, one of the things I decided to act on immediately was to share my surgical plans with a select few of our closest friends. That very night, during a previously scheduled cookout, I broke the news of my impending surgery to three of our closest friends, Kerry "Crow" Crawford, and Marc and Kim Mercer.

Crow was a career law enforcement officer and he looked every bit the part. Standing six feet three inches tall, his height and barrel chest offered clear indication that he was quite capable of defending the ground he stood on. As a matter of fact, Crow served as one of his department's certified "hand-to-hand defensive tactics" instructors. He has mastered the use of pressure points and submission holds that can make a grown man cry faster than watching *Little House on the Prairie* reruns.

Crow had known for months about the severity of my physical troubles. He, along with the Mercers, was one of my very few confidants. His training as a professional hostage negotiator allowed him the dual skills of compassionate listening and honest straight talk. On a number of occasions he had used both liberally on me. He was ever quick to remind me that my health and family were more important than speaking engagements and travel schedules. Crow was always a good sounding board.

Besides Crow, I shared my surgical intentions with Marc and Kim Mercer. Marc, Crow and I spent a lot of time together. We were a sort of modern day version of The Three Stooges. It was hard to miss us when we were together. The physical contrasts were striking.

As mentioned, Crow stood six feet three inches tall. Still, he was towered over by Marc who measured a whopping six feet nine inches, not counting his three to four inches of full, wavy hair! We would remind Marc that it was time for a haircut whenever the ceiling fan in our family room brushed his locks as he passed under.

Now compare those two giants with normal little me at five feet nine inches. Whenever Mercer and I walked together, it was not unusual to hear someone off in the distance whistling the theme song from the old *The Andy Griffith Show*. I often felt an overpowering urge to bend down, pick up a rock and "chuck" it in a lake somewhere.

But, like Crow, Marc was one of my dearest friends. Though he was concerned about my condition, he never allowed me the opportunity to feel sorry for myself. My frequent dashes to the men's room when we were together were commonly met with good-natured needling. He teased that my age (I am about three or four years older than he), not IBD, was the real cause of my problems. His caustic wit and mocking good humor were like medicine for my spirits.

Then there was Kim, Marc's wife. Kim was Susan's best friend and the closest thing to a younger sister that I'd ever had. About four years younger than I, Kim was a beautiful woman—tall and shapely, with a ready smile and lively eyes. She wore her hair stylishly short and always blonde.

I liked to tease Kim by asking her to describe the color of her hair. Her response was always the same. "N-9," she would say with great pleasure. "I just tell my hairdresser that I want my hair to stay N-9!" She made me laugh. I loved her creativity, energy and zest for life.

Kim was more than a friend. She was also a vital part of our business. Kim had worked with Susan and me in our speaking business for more than five years when my affliction with IBD began. Working daily in close quarters, she was more aware of my deteriorating condition than anyone other than Susan. During the entire period Kim's concern, compassion and loyalty were simply unsurpassed.

Crow, Marc and Kim all received the news of my intent to pursue the surgical route, much as I expected, with immediate and unquestioned support. They cried with us. Then they dried their tears and committed to stand strong with us. Though there were no concrete assignments to be made, each stood ready to do whatever he or she could to help. At a time of significant uncertainty, their friendship and availability served to sustain me. It was wonderful knowing the three of them were there for us whenever and however we might need them.

The more my mind was occupied with thoughts of my upcoming trip to Cleveland and the surgery to follow, the more the days sped by. There was so much to do and time was quickly slipping away.

Susan and I decided to wait until the Labor Day weekend, just two weeks away, to tell our extended family members in Kentucky about my decision. We had already made plans to be in Princeton that weekend for the reunion marking twenty-five years since my Caldwell County High School graduation. I thought it better to tell my family face-to-face, rather than by way of some unsuspecting telephone call.

As a family, we made the seven hundred plus mile drive to Kentucky for the reunion weekend, arriving the Thursday evening before Labor Day. The trip was physically and mentally arduous, requiring frequent and urgent "rest" stops along the way.

Nevertheless the weekend proved to be a festive time, featuring receptions, a golf outing and a dinner/dance. Though my flare-up raged on, laughter, conversation and reminiscing with old friends served to brighten my outlook and redirect my thinking away from my ever rumbling, overactive gut.

Not wanting to do anything to dampen the spirit of the occasion, I opted to wait to tell my closest high school friends and former classmates, Anna Jo (Pickens) Wyman, Jim McDaniel and Anthony Stallins, about my decision. I resolved to call them following my Cleveland visit and share all the relevant details then. I knew they would want to know.

No such option existed with my extended family. They had to be told—and soon. So in the brief time available between reunion events, I shared my current state with each family member, one-on-one. Though I had intended to be as matter-of-fact and non-emotional as possible, I soon learned that I had not figured in the "love factor" heavily enough.

In the interest of time, Susan shared the news of my impending surgery with her mom and dad without me present. Later my father-in-law, Merlin Alsobrook, sought me out.

"Phillip, I owe you an apology. I'm sorry," he said, conveying genuine emotion. "I had no idea how serious your condition had become. I now realize I've taken the entire matter much too lightly. I was aware you were having problems now and then, but I never dreamed it would result in surgery. I just expected that you would eventually get better over time. Please forgive me and know that your mother-in-law and I will make ourselves available to do whatever we can to help."

Merlin's words were unexpected but heartfelt. His apology was unnecessary but I appreciated it. His sentiments caused me to re-evaluate my earlier decision to shield those I loved from the reality of my condition.

It had been easy to conceal my condition from my family due to the miles separating us and the infrequency of our visits. But was it the right thing to do? Will my family now forever wonder what else I am keeping from them? These are the people who love and care most about me. Will they resent how I have treated them? Have I treated them fairly? Is this how I would have wanted them to handle the situation if the shoe were on the other foot?

My mother was even more emotional. When I explained to her that I was fairly certain that surgery was imminent and that it would require the total removal of my colon, the fear and uncertainty of this new information was immediately etched on her face.

"Phil, is it cancer?" she blurted out.

"No, Mom. I promise you it's not cancer."

I began to reassure her, while explaining all that I had learned about my condition and the treatments available to me. I explained that the ensuing surgery would be life changing, but not life-threatening. As she regained her composure, she quickly volunteered to come to Florida to stay with the kids while Susan and I were in Cleveland for the surgery. She wanted to help.

When I shared the news with my sister Ellen (seven years older than I), and my younger brother Dan (eleven years younger than I), both showed great concern coupled with controlled emotion. They wanted to know all the facts and details, as well as what they could do to help. I assured them there was nothing I wanted more from them than their prayers. It was obvious that they cared.

Without question, the most surprising response came from my other brother Mark. Only seventeen months separate us in age, with me being older. Due to the closeness of our ages, Mark and I spent our childhood doing almost everything together. And we complemented each other in many ways. What one lacked, the other provided. He was big and strong, I was small and quick. He was quiet and reserved, I was loud and outgoing. All things considered, together we made a pretty good team.

As we got older though, we drifted apart somewhat, in pursuit of our own individual interests and friends. I finished college and left the area to pursue my career, while Mark chose to stay in the Princeton area. It bothered me that we weren't as close as we once were. And I imagined that it bothered Mark, too. But we never really discussed it. We just built our separate lives with casual, infrequent interaction.

But I will never forget that Saturday afternoon when I shared my news with Mark. As the magnitude of my words began to sink in, to my surprise Mark could barely contain himself. I had hardly gotten the words out when the tears began to cascade down his cheeks. Through tears and sobs, Mark told me over and over how much he loved me. He told me how concerned he was for me and how badly he wanted me to be better so we could enjoy more time together.

I had been successful in keeping my emotions in check as I shared my plans with the others. But with Mark, I failed. There in a tiny,

Princeton hotel room I reconnected with Mark and experienced once again the depth of his love for me. Together we stood embracing each other tightly as the tears freely flowed.

Long after the weekend was over and we were back in Florida, I still remembered that time with my family, especially with Mark. I could still feel the warmth of his tears on my cheek during our embrace.

Most importantly, I continued to feel the very essence of love and support all around me. To a person, each family member had wanted to know specifically what he or she could do to help me during this difficult period. That reconfirmation served as a great encouragement as I prepared for my upcoming adventure.

The days continued to pass quickly until September 14, 2000, at 5:30 a.m. I pulled out of my driveway, headed for the Orlando airport. About three and a half-hours later I was seated aboard a Continental Airlines flight winging my way toward my destination—Cleveland Hopkins International Airport, Cleveland, Ohio.

Once on the ground in Cleveland, I made my way through the terminal and out to the waiting shuttle bus that would carry me to the off-site Avis rental car lot. It seemed strange not to be lugging several pieces of bulky luggage, my normal traveling custom. But this was no normal speaking engagement. This was a scouting trip. I was here for the purpose of scouting out surgeons.

You see, as difficult as my months-long struggle with colitis had been for me, it had also taught me a few things. One of the best lessons I had learned involved the importance of choosing the right physician. I believed then—and now—there were few reasons, if any, why I should settle for any doctor that I found in any way to be unsatisfactory.

I realize choosing the right physician can be confusing and there are many different ways to go about the process. I suppose some people are willing to settle for the first physician they happen upon as they thumb through the Yellow Pages. Can't you almost hear the conversation now?

"Mable, how am I supposed to know which of these doctors is a good one? There's gotta be more than two dozen gynecologists listed here. Hey, wait a minute. This Dr. Stephen T. Aardvark III, M.D., (the first alphabetical listing) sounds fine to me. What do you think? Do you want me to give him a call and schedule you an appointment?"

Sounds ridiculous, doesn't it? My guess is that Mable won't be terribly excited about young Dr. Aardvark. Before Mable selects her primary caregiver, she will probably want more information than the phone book provides.

I think it's safe to assume that most intelligent human beings when hiring a professional—lawyer, accountant, contractor, mechanic, plumber, speaker—will consider a number of variables before making their informed choice. Most of us will want to have specific questions answered relative to the professional's education/training, years of experience, areas of specialization, professional reputation and satisfied clients, not to mention the anticipated cost of the services to be rendered. Yet, for most of us, high on the list of unwritten qualifications is the professional's ability (and willingness) to communicate freely and openly with us.

Since becoming an adult, I have taken the responsibility of choosing my primary physicians very seriously. I know what I want. And I know what I won't tolerate!

For example, I remember going to a doctor several years ago as a result of some sort of "flu du jour" from which I was suffering. When I finally saw the doctor, he entered the examination room without so much as a greeting. He walked purposely to where I was sitting, put his stethoscope to my chest and gruffly instructed me to take a deep breath.

I did as I was told. But before I could even exhale that first breath, the stethoscope was out of his ears and the doctor had wheeled around and was headed for the door, giving instructions to the attending nurse over his shoulder on his way out. Just like that, he was gone!

Without speaking a word to me other than "Take a deep breath," the doctor left the room. We were together, literally, less than thirty seconds. There was absolutely no opportunity for questions, comments, reassurance—nothing. Even the nurse wore a baffled look of helplessness as she gave me the injection and presented me with my bill for forty-five dollars.

I was left to wonder, *Was there something special going on in another part of the office complex that required his immediate presence? Was he preoccupied with a difficult case? Was there some sort of emergency of which I was unaware? If so, why didn't he just say so?*

Or was this just a thoughtless, arrogant jerk, masquerading as someone who supposedly cares about my well being? Maybe he had more important patients to attend to. Maybe he was late for a golf game. Maybe his bunions hurt. Whatever the case, it's obvious he had very little regard for me as a person.

I will never know what was going on with that doctor that day. He made no effort to let me know. So I was left to draw my conclusions based on emotion, not information. As a result, though I didn't have the pleasure of telling him to his face, in my car on the way home that day I fired that callused caregiver. That's right. I fired him. I had every right to do so. I fired him by choosing never to give his practice my business again.

I had reached a point in my life where I was not easily buffaloed. I had come to the realization that position, status, reputation and expertise are all important. But a positive, trusting professional relationship is built on all of these, *plus* effective two-way communication. The medical profession has always placed great importance in this concept. They even coined a phrase that is well known to all of us. The phrase? "Bedside manner."

But this careless caregiver apparently chose to cast all those time-honored conventions aside. His self-absorbed attitude made me suspicious of future physicians with whom I had not yet developed a trust-based relationship. *His* ignorance of or blatant disregard for the need to establish basic, elementary rapport with a new patient caused me to be wary of initial encounters with *future* doctors.

Please don't misunderstand. I didn't want this first meeting with Dr. Lavery to go badly. Quite the contrary. I needed help. I had been advised that help resided within the hallowed halls of the Cleveland Clinic. My search had brought me to this place.

But I came with an expectation that needed to be met for me to be satisfied. I knew expertise *and* bedside manner existed in the healthcare arena. I knew because Dr. Glen Morgan had both. So did Dr. Richard Truesdale. And this Dr. Ian Lavery would have them too—or I would continue my search elsewhere.

I started my car and referred once more to the map provided me earlier by the Cleveland Clinic. I was soon motoring northward on I-71 toward the downtown area. Just south of the city I followed my directions and turned east on Carnegie Avenue. Eventually I found myself in the heart of the Cleveland Clinic campus. The well-kept grounds covered at least twelve city blocks. Several modern-looking high rise buildings rose from these parcels of land.

I wheeled my vehicle into the Euclid Avenue Parking Garage and found an available space. From there I continued on foot, in search of the "Crile Building, A111." After getting my bearings, a two-minute walk due east landed me at my destination. I rode the elevator to the eleventh floor. I approached the desk to sign in. They were expecting me.

Consistent with every other first time doctor's visit I had ever experienced, a mound of initial paperwork awaited completion. I took the forms and retired to a far corner of the room. There I took a seat with my back facing the window overlooking the courtyard more than one hundred feet below.

Before long I had satisfactorily completed the forms. I returned them to the desk and was told to rest comfortably until my name was called. I retook my seat and began the process of familiarizing myself with my surroundings.

The waiting area was considerably larger than those found in private practices. It was designed to handle a great number of patients as efficiently as possible. Surrounding the waiting area were offices or stations that patients were being called into regularly. Some of these stations were simply partitioned sections of the waiting room floor. They reminded me of the office cubicles depicted in the popular *Dilbert* comic strip. I half expected Dr. Wally or some Pointy-Haired administrator to poke his head out at any moment.

The area was a beehive of activity. People of all shapes, sizes, colors, ages and apparent states of health were present.

My attention was drawn to one gentleman in particular. I guessed him to be in his mid-60s. I watched him shuffle into the waiting area from the elevators with considerable difficulty. His middle-aged female companion was by his side, paying special attention to his every need.

I wonder what his story is? I'll bet he's coming back for a post-operative checkup. Man, he sure looks fragile.

I wonder how long it has been since his surgery? It can't be very long or surely he would be moving around better than that.

I wonder if his surgery was anything like the one I will be having? If so, will I be getting around like that? Surely not. I'm probably twenty years younger than he is.

I wonder if he would mind my asking him a few questions? He looks nice enough...but, no, I better not. He doesn't look up to conversation with a stranger right now.

Before any of my questions were answered and while still more were forming, this particular John Doe was called and then led by a pretty thirty-something nurse through the door beside the processing desk into the bowels of the office. I watched him shuffle off before turning my attention to first one, then another of the people waiting patiently for their names to be called. Each time I tried to imagine their malady while working to convince myself that their physical problem was much worse than mine.

After about an hour of waiting, I finally heard a familiar name being called.

"Phillip Van Hooser. Patient Phillip Van Hooser!"

I looked up and saw a young nurse standing in the doorway, file folder in hand, scanning the busy waiting room. As I recognized my name, I began gathering up the paperwork I had brought with me. My movement caught the nurse's eye.

"Mr. Van Hooser?"

"Yes," I responded.

"Mr. Van Hooser, if you will, please follow me and we will get you started."

The young woman told me her name before leading me down a short hall and into a small, cramped examination room. Once inside, she asked me to take a seat.

"Mr. Van Hooser, I understand you're from Florida. Welcome to Cleveland. I have several forms to complete and a number of questions to ask you before Dr. Lavery sees you. First, I see you're carrying an envelope. Is it, by chance, your medical records from your physician in Florida?"

"Yes, it is."

"Good. I'll take those from you."

For the next twenty minutes or so this nurse asked question after question, writing down my responses in specific detail. Her questions ran the full gamut, including my family's medical history, my dietary habits and my current medications. Still more information she simply verified from the materials I provided her. But by far the majority of our time together was spent revisiting, step by step, my experiences before and since being diagnosed with ulcerative colitis.

I tried to answer her questions as completely as I could. In doing so, I surprised myself with the depth of chronological detail I was able to provide. I successfully provided definitive answers to most of the what, when, where and how much questions she posed.

I was especially surprised and pleased at the grasp of the medical lingo I had acquired during the past seventeen months. As she asked technical questions, I was able to understand and respond using the appropriate medical terminology. Apparently, all my independent research and reading were paying off. If this experience had been some sort of college level class, I appeared to be well prepared for the final examination.

When the nurse had exhausted all of her questions and completed each form, she closed the file and stood to leave.

"Mr. Van Hooser, I will share this information with Dr. Lavery. He will be in shortly to see you. Please make yourself comfortable."

As the nurse left me alone in the room, I began to feel just the opposite—somewhat uncomfortable, ill at ease. In the waiting room there had been activity and other people to focus and concentrate on. Here, all I had to focus on was diplomas and tongue depressors. In the quiet solitude of this room, I determined there was nothing to do but sit and think—and pray.

"Lord, you know that this has been a difficult period for me. But you have helped me through it. You have provided a loving wife to support me. You have provided a wonderful medical team to treat me.

And through it all, you have given me the necessary strength to endure. Now, Lord, I ask that you help me connect with this surgeon in a positive way. Thank you for helping me..."

Somewhere during the course of my prayer, I heard the shuffling of several sets of feet just outside my door. Soon the door opened and in they walked. I was expecting one. I got four.

"Mr. Van Hooser, my name is Dr. Ian Lavery."

There standing before me was the man who had occupied so much time in my thoughts during the past month. Three lab-coat-laden young strangers accompanied him. I immediately began the process of sizing them all up.

Lavery's physical stature was not overpowering. He appeared to be in his mid to late 50's and of average height and weight. He wore a white lab coat with his name stitched in black over his heart. Against the bright white of his coat, his face shone brightly, the obvious result of too much recent sun. I remember thinking that he had an appearance that would blend easily into most crowds. His most distinct feature was an engaging accent, the product of his New Zealand roots, I would learn later.

As for the other three, all were young. I guessed them to be in their mid to late 20's. All three wore bright white lab coats, too, except there were no names neatly stitched over their hearts. Their coats were blank. Apparently they had not yet "lettered." I immediately surmised they were rookies—medical students in training.

My mind raced back to my father. My dad had died thirteen years earlier, the victim of one final massive heart attack. Prior to his death my father had been hospitalized with various heart problems on several occasions. It was then that I had encountered my first white-coated rookies.

These specialists-to-be had always intrigued me. They seemed prone to follow the designated physician-in-charge, like baby ducklings follow their mother. Always careful to remain close enough to their leader to consume any random tidbits they might happen upon. Yet not so close as to be involved in an embarrassing pileup should the main guy stop abruptly.

These three young students had followed Dr. Lavery into this room on yet another mission of discovery. I suspected they had been casually briefed concerning my condition before entering. It was obvious I was alive and still kicking, but I could just as easily have been a cadaver. At this point in their educational process I surmised that my specific medical condition made very little difference to them. This examination room was their extended classroom. A place for them to observe, to experience, to learn—that's all.

But I expected more. I wanted them to feel, too. I wanted them to feel what I was feeling. I wanted to them to care as much about my complete recovery as I cared, as my family cared and as my friends cared. I wanted them to know that I was not just another case study. I intended for them to get to know me, if only for this brief encounter.

As I evaluated the way the four entered the room, it was obvious that Dr. Lavery had no intention of wasting valuable time on the unnecessary introductions of the three. So what did I do? That's right. I introduced myself to Dr. Lavery and the three.

"Hello, Doctor," I said as I reached and shook his hand. "Please call me Phil."

I then immediately turned and extended my hand to each of the three, introducing myself and asking each his hometown and specialty.

Number one: "Hi, I'm Bob. I'm from Baltimore, Maryland, and I'm a 'fellow' in the field of colorectal surgery."

The way Bob emphasized the word "fellow" made me know that he was impressed with his position and that he thought maybe I should be, too. However, the title meant nothing to me. On the other hand, if this young fellow were able to help me with my problem, now that would be impressive.

"It's nice to meet you, Bob. I love going to Baltimore and watching baseball at Camden Yard," I said casually before turning to the next.

Number two: "I'm Steven from Asheville, North Carolina. I'm working to become a gastroenterologist."

I had become intimately familiar with the field of gastroenterology in recent months. I sensed no overt arrogance or cockiness in Steven's demeanor.

Maybe this will be a good one. Possibly another Truesdale.

"Steven, it's a pleasure. You certainly come from a beautiful part of the country. I've spoken at the Grove Park Inn on a number of occasions."

Finally, tucked away in the far corner, number three spoke up.

Number three: "My name is Paul. I'm from Cincinnati and I'm finishing my studies in gynecology."

Number three's response caught me totally by surprise. I just looked at him while trying to determine if I had heard correctly. Satisfied I had, I dug for more information.

"Gynecology?" I asked with amazement. "Is there something I need to know that you guys aren't telling me?"

"Don't worry, it's just part of the curriculum," he replied with a toothy grin.

It was just the right touch to break whatever tension I might have been experiencing. We all laughed.

When I turned again to face Dr. Lavery, he had taken a seat and was peering into my file, efficiently reviewing the paperwork in his possession. I slid back into the seat I had occupied earlier. I sat waiting for him to speak.

"Mr. Van Hooser, excuse me, I mean Phil. Your records indicate you have been diagnosed and treated for the past several months for an advanced case of ulcerative colitis. Is that right?" he asked, without looking up from the file.

"Yes, that's right," I said. I could sense the tone of the conversation turn more serious.

"Your records also indicate that you have recently been determined to be steroid dependent by your attending physician in Florida. Is that right?"

"That's right."

"Has your physician provided you a detailed explanation of the type of surgery that is required to correct your problem?" Dr. Lavery glanced up from the file as I offered my response.

"Yes, he has. We have talked at length about proctocolectomy surgery. He has explained the process of creating a pouch from the ileum. He has candidly shared the related risks and benefits. He also told me that should I opt for this surgery, the Cleveland Clinic's reputation in this area is second to none. That's why I'm here today."

Dr. Lavery listened carefully to my response before returning his eyes to the file, which he pondered a while longer. I tried desperately to read his mind, to anticipate his thoughts. I could not. Finally, he pushed back from the file and stared at me.

I could never have predicted Dr. Lavery's next words, as simple and direct as they were. I would not have been surprised if he had challenged the fact I was there in the first place. Maybe I didn't look sick enough to him.

I would also have not been surprised had he launched into an infomercial-type sales job, trumpeting the Colorectal Surgery Department's unsurpassed superiority while using a mountain of hand-gathered facts, figures and statistics.

He did neither. Instead, he looked at me and asked a question.

"Phil, how can I help you?"

I had heard these same words so many times in recent days from family and friends. All were sincere and well meaning. Yet when Dr. Lavery spoke the words, I knew he could help.

"Doc, you can give me my life back. I am told that the surgery you perform here cures ulcerative colitis. I want to be cured. Do you think you can help me?"

Dr. Lavery smiled and said, "I believe we can."

My heart soared.

I spent another twenty minutes or so in the company of Dr. Lavery and his understudies. During that time the doctor performed a digital anal examination to be sure there were no signs of Crohn's disease present.

I stressed that I would like the surgery to take place before Thanksgiving so I would be able to recuperate during the holidays—a traditionally slow period for speakers. We settled on Friday, November 10th, 2000 as the date for the surgery. Dr. Lavery gave me a full packet of pre-surgery materials to review and promised more to come.

In less than an hour I was headed back to the airport for my return to Florida. I was excited. Help was on the way.

8

With A Little Help From My Friends

The printed letterhead proudly proclaimed from whence the letter had come: *The Cleveland Clinic Foundation*. It read…

October 9, 2000

Glen Morgan, M.D.
2760 SE 17th St.
Ocala, FL 34471

NAME: Van Hooser, Phillip
CLINIC NO.: 3-092-317-0
DATE OF SERVICE: 09/14/2000

Dear Dr. Morgan:

I saw your patient, Mr. Phillip Van Hooser, in consultation on September 14, 2000. He is a 43-year-old man with a two-year history of ***mucosal colitis*** *that has not responded to good conventional medical therapy. He was considering surgical intervention.*

When I examined Mr. Van Hooser, I confirmed your findings. There was moderate inflammation of the rectum to 20cm, which had the typical appearance of chronic mucosal ulcerative colitis. He would be a suitable candidate for a proctocolectomy and a ***J-pouch ileoanal anastomosis****. I discussed this with him and arrangements have been made for him to be admitted to The Cleveland Clinic for surgery on November 10, 2000. I will keep you informed of his progress.*

Yours faithfully,

Ian C. Lavery, M.D.
Staff Surgeon

This official, two-paragraph letter bore the classic markings of one professional dutifully communicating with another. In this case, the professionals happened to be caregivers. Let me explain.

First, the correspondence was appropriately succinct and detached. In "doctor-speak," the final two sentences of paragraph one—twenty-nine words in total—summed up my more than *500 days* of physical suffering and psychological uncertainty. And there was nary a twinge of emotion to be found on the page anywhere.

Second, the correspondence was objective and specific. It sufficiently answered, with appropriate detail, all the *who*, *what*, *when*, *where* and *why* questions regarding the surgical actions that would soon be undertaken on my behalf.

Finally, the leisurely timing of the correspondence gave indication that the letter was intended to be proper documentation rather than personal communication. It seemed written more for a file than for a person. Drafted a full four weeks after our initial Cleveland consultation, the letter arrived just under a month before the actual surgery was scheduled to take place.

Not that this professional, though somewhat impersonal, manner of communication is bad. It's not. In fact, it happens every day. It simply is what it is.

However, mine was not the luxury of having a leisurely period during which I could communicate the reality of my experience to interested parties in a succinct, detached, objective, totally unemotional manner. On the contrary. I was consumed by the experience. Every day, dozens of times during the day for two full months, I was confronted with some reality of my upcoming surgery and all that it entailed.

But it wasn't just about me. I had long resisted, but the time had now come to include and involve others in this, my medical adventure. And it began quickly and in earnest upon my return home following my consultation with Dr. Lavery.

That night Susan and I lay talking in the quiet darkness of our bedroom. I recounted the experiences of my Cleveland trip in great detail. Susan, of course, wanted to know everything.

When my memory bank was finally depleted, we paused momentarily and then launched into the process of considering critical plans that needed to be made. There was so much to be done. We both agreed the first thing on the agenda was to inform our children. That inevitability could be delayed no longer.

The next morning found the Van Hooser household to be its normal beehive of activity. The kids, less than three weeks removed from their summer vacation, were busily preparing for another day of formal schooling. Each approached his or her day with a slightly different attitude.

For almost three weeks now Joe had been strutting like a young peacock. He was thoroughly enjoying the feeling of finally being one of the "big men" on campus. As a thirteen-year-old eighth grader, all that stood between him and high school was this, his third and final year of middle school. He was confident, enthusiastic and anxious to grow up and get on with life.

Sarah found herself on the other end of the middle school spectrum. As a sixth grader her confidence was just being formed as she adjusted to her new middle school routine. The first few days of the semester brought an unfamiliar rotating class schedule, along with a new slate of teachers and classmates. Like many eleven-year-old girls she was somewhat anxious, excitable and emotionally high-strung.

Then there was Sophie—our baby. Having turned six exactly two weeks earlier, Sophie had the dubious distinction of being the youngest member of her first grade class. Undeterred, she was excited and enthusiastic about every aspect of her budding academic experience. From counting to coloring, from recitation to recess—she absolutely loved the entire educational package.

So beyond the normal energy that three healthy, active children bring to a home, there was noticeable excitement and anticipation regarding the specific activities of the day ahead. As we gathered around the breakfast table, our mealtime custom, we paused and gave thanks for and asked blessings on the food we were about to enjoy and for the day we were about to encounter.

Silently, I breathed an additional prayer asking for clarity and composure regarding the message that was mine to share. With "amen" still hanging in the air, spoons and glasses were taken up and the assault on the Frosted Flakes, Pop-Tarts, grapes and orange juice began.

Conversation at mealtime was always an intriguing proposition. Whenever two adults, a teenager, a pre-teen and a first grader—all competitive extroverts—vie for the conversation spotlight, one never quite knew what the results might be. On various occasions I've seen infinite combinations of mealtime chatter during which laughter erupts, dreams get revealed, stories get interrupted, feelings get hurt, accomplishments get applauded, ideas get criticized, creativity gets rewarded, glasses get spilled, individuals get teased, jokes get ruined and tears get shed. On this particular morning my greatest fear was that innocence would get lost.

"Well, guys, how's life this morning?" I asked.

This was my standard, first-thing-in-the-morning question. They had all heard it posed many times before. Depending on the child and depending on the morning, it could be alternately met with enthusiastic, subdued and even sarcastic responses. But it usually served as a good way to break the early morning ice.

"Great!" was Sarah's brief, but perky reply.

Joe's guttural uttering was more restrained, even acerbic. "Just peachy," he said.

It was Sophie who provided me the opening with her enthusiastic, "I'm great, Daddy. How was your trip?"

"It was good, Soaf. Thanks for asking," I said with a measure of self-manufactured enthusiasm. "But there is something very important I need to talk to the three of you about this morning. So listen carefully. Okay?"

My comment caught them off guard. They all turned their attention to me in a suspicious, somewhat questioning manner. I could read their minds: Is he serious or somehow setting us up? You see, breakfast was not traditionally when we discussed "very important" matters. And even when we did, they were not usually announced as such.

"Kids, I want to ask you a question. Have you noticed that I've been feeling bad?"

"I didn't," came Sophie's quick reply. She responded in much the same way that I imagined she would have had her teacher asked her a question in class.

"What's wrong?" Sarah asked cautiously.

"He's had diarrhea for a long time," Joe said to his sisters, a hint of disgust evident in his voice. He then turned to me and asked,

"What's wrong, Dad? Are you worse?"

"Yeah, as a matter of fact, I am," I said honestly. "I need to let you in on something before you hear it from someone else. In a couple of months, I'm going to have an operation. It's pretty serious, but listen to me. I'm not going to die or anything like that. I just need the surgery so I won't have to go to the bathroom as much as I do now."

An unusual, thus uncomfortable, silence fell around the table. Joe stared directly at me while Sarah diverted her eyes to her cereal bowl. Directly across from me, Sophie's eyes began to puddle. I continued my explanation in an even voice.

"Listen now, there's no reason to worry. I'm going to be fine. I just didn't want you to hear the news from somebody else. Now if you have any questions, I'd like to hear them."

Sarah spoke first.

"Will the surgery be here in Ocala?" she asked.

"No, I'll be going to Cleveland, Ohio. There's a hospital up there that specializes in the type of surgery that I need. I will be up there for a week or so and then I'll be home again."

"Is that why you went to Cleveland yesterday?" Joe asked.

"Yeah, it is. I just went up there to meet the surgeon and to make sure I felt good about what they can do for me. Now I'm convinced it's the right place to have this operation done."

"When will we leave to go to Cleveland?" Sarah wondered.

"You guys aren't going. You can't afford to miss that much school. Just Mom and I are going."

"Who will take care of us?" Sophie asked with a weepy voice.

Susan jumped in before I had the chance to respond.

"Don't worry, Sophie. Your grandmother is coming down from Kentucky to stay with you all. She'll be sure you make it to school as well as to all your dance lessons and baseball practices. She'll take good care of all of you while I am taking care of your Daddy." Then Susan added with a mischievous smirk, "You all remember how he was with his toe!"

All three of the kids immediately perked up. They began to nod, smile and then giggle. It was one of those "you had to be there" family things.

A couple of summers earlier, I had an in-grown toenail that became infected just before we left on a family vacation to Yellowstone National Park. For the entire two-week trip I limped all over Montana, playfully exaggerating my ailment and milking it for all the sympathy it was worth. Soon, Susan and the kids caught on and, in turn, began to tease me unmercifully. Since that time, if I happen to even casually complain of a personal ailment, someone is bound to leap at the chance to say something like, "Oh, the poor baby's toe is hurting again," followed by derisive laughter. It's all done in good-natured fun.

Susan's comment hit the mark. It did a wonderful job of breaking the tension of the moment. When their laughter subsided, I wrapped the conversation up.

"Well, that's all there is to it," I added. "If you want to know anything else, just ask your mom or me. Okay?"

"Okay," they all replied in unison, once again taking up their spoons.

Having the kids know the truth was a great relief to me. Greater still was their response to the news. I am totally convinced that children take their emotional lead from the influential adults in their lives. They tend to respond emotionally to events in much the same way they observe their parents, teachers and coaches responding. The fact that Susan and I chose to share the news of my upcoming surgery in a matter-of-fact manner, even using humor, somehow relieved the kids' emotional burden and allowed them to relax and process the news rationally.

In the days ahead I selectively shared my "news" with the people closest to me. I found their responses to be encouraging, flattering, surprising, and, on occasion, downright overwhelming.

For example, as I had promised myself previously, I called three of my closest friends from high school. Each understood why I had withheld "the news" from them during our class reunion a few weeks earlier. But now Jim McDaniel, Anthony Stallins and Anna Jo Wyman wanted to know what they could do to help.

I assured each that knowing their prayers were with me was enough. Still, a few days before I left for the hospital, I received a humorous card from Anna Jo. Tucked insider were five crisp twenty-dollar bills. The accompanying note said that the cash should be used for Susan's meal money while in Cleveland.

I immediately phoned Anna Jo.

"Anna Jo, it's too much. And honestly, we really don't need it," I told her.

"Phillip Van Hooser, you're my friend. Unfortunately, I won't be able to be there with you for the surgery. And I know you don't really need the money," she said, "but I really need to give it to you. This is something I want to do."

She explained that fifteen years earlier, following the birth of her first child, Joseph—a Downs Syndrome baby—many weeks had been spent in and out of hospitals. During those days certain people had provided gifts of cash to help defray the cost of travel, hotels and meals out. She had never forgotten those people and their generous, selfless acts of kindness. Anna Jo was now one of those people I, too, will never forget.

Another person I shared "the news" with was my professional videographer, a wonderful gentleman named Bob Ramey. Other than myself, Bob knew the content of my professional work better than any other person on the face of the earth. He had every reason to. For more than ten years Bob had spent literally hundreds of hours viewing and reviewing, frame by frame, dozens of my speeches and training programs. These were programs he had been hired to film, edit and convert to various video products. I respected Bob's professionalism and had grown to appreciate him as a friend.

I stopped by Bob's office for the purpose of explaining my

current need to alter our project development schedule as a result of my upcoming surgery. As closely as we had worked together to that point, Bob had been unaware of my deteriorating physical condition. Yet, his response to "the news" was immediate.

Bob offered to drive his motor home all the way from Florida to Cleveland for the sole purpose of comfortably chauffeuring Susan and me back to Florida following the surgery. His offer was not an idle one. Bob cared about me. I was touched.

Probably the most overwhelming widespread support I received was from my spiritual family. During and after my period of hospitalization, I learned of dozens of congregations around the country that had me listed on their local prayer calendars. I had been placed there by an unknown number of caring individuals who were aware of my current need. To this day, I testify to the power of those heartfelt prayers of intercession.

But no congregation prayed harder or cared more about my situation, my family and me than did the church to which we belonged. First Baptist Church, Ocala, Florida, had been our spiritual oasis for more than fourteen years. We were happy there. We were being fed there. And we enjoyed serving there.

Our children were actively involved in the youth and music programs. Susan served in a variety of roles, including being a key member of the church's Personnel Committee. I served on the local Deacon body and taught a weekly adult Bible study class.

As a matter of fact, on any given Sunday, our class would attract between 300 and 350 eager Bible students. These men and women ranged in age from nineteen to ninety. Their faces were black, brown and white. There were singles, couples, divorcees, widows and widowers.

They were students and retirees. They wore white collars and blue collars. They were educated and uneducated. They were Yankees and Rednecks, Cowboys and Hillbillies. But they all shared one thing in common—they loved their Lord.

Though ours was a Baptist church, at least half of this class's membership had received some measure of prior religious instruction by way of other denominations including Methodist, Presbyterian, Church of God, Church of Christ, Lutheran and Nazarene. Broader still, a handful of our members had some personal affiliation with Catholicism, Judaism, Buddhism or Islam.

The diversity of the group offered wonderful opportunities for in-depth scriptural study coupled with stimulating group discussion. Sunday after Sunday, for more than three years, I had looked forward to leading these believers in Bible study, prayer and fellowship. I had looked forward to these sessions that is, until the morning arrived when it came time to share "my news" with the collective gathering.

Week after week, as a class, our habit had been to publicly acknowledge friends, family members, coworkers and even strangers who were in special need of prayer support due to some critical situation they were facing. I often led those prayers. Yet week after week, for more than a year and a half, I had kept my condition from these wonderful people—my friends. Though I coveted their prayers, I had intentionally concealed my needs from them. Why, I wasn't quite sure.

If I disclose my areas of weakness, maybe they will think I am weak. If I tell them what is really going on with me, will they feel sorry for me? That's not what I want. Will they question the strength of my faith? I know that the Lord knows my needs—that's enough. There really is no sense in getting too many other people involved.

My thoughts I could conceal. The day finally arrived, however, when I could no longer conceal my secret from this special group of people. The calendar was working against me.

I stood before the class and came clean. I revealed my extended struggle with ulcerative colitis—what it was and what it had done to me. I continued by explaining how the struggle would soon culminate with my scheduled surgery. In general terms I shared that the removal of my colon was necessary and that a three or four month period of incapacitation would certainly follow. I assured them that I would be back teaching just as soon as I physically could, but that in the meantime the church's pastor, Brother Ed Johnson, had graciously agreed to lead the class during my absence.

The class received this news in stunned, muted silence. I had "seemed so healthy," several told me later. But my revelation served to reinforce the reality that all of us have issues—not all of them physical, of course—but issues nonetheless, that we intentionally shield from public view. But should we? Is it really a good idea in the long run to be so secretive? Are we always able to shoulder the burden alone?

Their lips spoke not a word, but their eyes said plenty. And what I heard their eyes saying was revealing.

Why have you kept this secret from us? We're your friends—your brothers and sisters. We love you. We care about you. We want to be here for you in your time of need. Do you not trust us? Now that we know, let us help you.

The information I shared with the class proved to be the key that unlocked their floodgates of love and concern. They were willing to be of service to us. They wanted to help, but until now I had withheld from them the opportunity.

The outpouring of love that followed was nothing short of amazing—and humbling. In the days leading up to the surgery, there were a dozen or more class members who did personal research to determine if other treatment options existed that I had not yet considered. Caring individuals provided information on every conceivable all-natural product, treatment, home remedy and holistic alternative. Though I chose to continue traveling the path of surgical intervention, I appreciated the outstanding efforts of each person.

Other class members focused their attention and actions on the welfare of my family. Knowing that our immediate family all lived in

Kentucky, several individuals stepped forward to volunteer to stay with our kids during our absence. When they learned that my mother would be filling that void, they shifted gears and immediately set about creating a list of volunteer chefs, each agreeing to prepare and deliver nightly meals to my family during my hospitalization and beyond. Our family was never better loved—and fed—than during that period.

About a week before we headed north to Ohio, we had visitors come to our home. A group of a dozen or so men from the church came to minister to us. A high school math teacher, Chairman of the Deacons and dear friend, Gary Stowers, led the group. With Gary were our pastor, several class members and a number of other deacons, along with my buddies Mercer and Crow.

There in the confines of our kitchen, with Susan and the kids present, these gentle men served up a heaping helping of love. Men—big, strong, powerfully built men—shared inspiring verses of scripture accompanied by encouraging words of love, support and appreciation. Before leaving they encircled me, and with their loving touch, prayed specifically for my well being and speedy recovery. They lifted in prayer the doctors, nurses and other professionals that would attend to my physical needs. Finally, they prayed for strength and peace for my family. The experience was overwhelming.

The culmination of our sendoff occurred on Sunday, November 5, 2000. Emotions ran high in class that morning as Brother Ed Johnson closed our Bible study with group prayer, asking God's blessings on me during the surgery the following Friday. I was blessed by the outpouring of love and affection.

At the conclusion of the class, members who would normally hustle off to don choir robes or hurry away to secure seats in the auditorium for the worship service, didn't. Not this morning.

This morning they formed an impromptu line that snaked its way around the room. Person after person, dozens in total, made their way to Susan and me to offer their personal voice of encouragement. Some simply reassured us that we would be in their continuing prayers.

Others hugged our necks, shook our hands or patted our shoulders lovingly. Some smiled, some wept. But all loved. It was one of the most moving experiences of my life. I will never forget how it made me feel.

As the line eventually wound down, I noticed Marc Mercer towering head, shoulders and chest above the crowd. Somehow it just seemed right that one of my dearest friends would be one of the last to wish me well before I headed out.

As Marc drew near, he grasped my hand and bent down to whisper something confidential in my ear. His words were meant for me alone. Others would not have understood.

"Phil, Phil, Phil, Phil, Phil," Marc said mockingly. "Enough already! I'm sick of hearing about you! Let's get this thing over with so we can talk about somebody else for a change. What do you say?"

I shot a quick glance at Marc's face. I saw a mile wide grin. That's all I needed. I exploded in laughter.

Marc was confident enough in our relationship and confident enough in the anticipated surgical outcome that he just felt it was time to have some fun with this thing. He was right.

It was a perfect sendoff. I knew my support group was with me. And as strange as it might sound, Marc's sarcastic remark was the highlight of a wonderful outpouring of affection—the cherry on the sundae, if you will.

I was ready. It was time to get this thing over with!

Mom had arrived a few days earlier and she and the kids had already settled comfortably into their temporary routine. As we said our good-byes, the kids seemed neither worried nor stressed. Apparently, we had prepared them well.

The evening of Wednesday, November 8, 2000, found Susan and me enjoying a quiet dinner in an out-of-the-way restaurant in Little

Italy, east of downtown Cleveland. Though I knew too well there would be a price to be paid for my indulgence, I decided to eat as if this were my last meal. For my colon, it would be.

Fearlessly, I ordered chicken parmigiana and a side of garlic bread. I savored every fried, spicy, greasy bite. I topped the meal off with ice cream with chocolate syrup. I drank caffeinated iced tea like it was going out of style. These delicacies were sure to cause me to make several trips to the bathroom during the night, but I was buoyed by the knowledge that in less than forty-eight hours, my colon would haunt me no longer.

When I first decided to have the surgery, I crafted a simple little plan in my head. It went something like this. Because the surgery would be a significant distance from home, Susan and I would simply slip out of town virtually unnoticed. During our absence Mom would oversee the kids, while Kim Mercer managed the business.

We would retire to the Cleveland Clinic for the necessary plumbing repairs. Once "fixed," I would emulate those old mixed-breed dogs I had grown up with in Farmersville, Kentucky.

Mutts. Curs. Strays. They may not have had an official pedigree, but I had always admired their constitution. They were low maintenance, expecting and requiring very little attention. When sick or injured, they would simply crawl under the porch until well enough to function again. No fanfare, just isolation.

That seemed like a good plan to me. After the necessary repairs had been made, I would crawl "under the porch" in Cleveland. Then when I was feeling better, Susan would bring me back to Florida to get on with our life. But, as we know, things don't always work out as we plan.

In fact, there had been fanfare before our departure—quite a bit of it. And surprisingly enough, it had served to bolster my spirits and confidence. As for Susan and me facing this situation in Cleveland alone, that wasn't going to happen either. We knew company was due to arrive the next afternoon.

It had all started innocently enough. Three or four weeks earlier my brother Mark had called from Kentucky to check on me.

"Phil, how are you feeling?"

"Oh, I'm doing alright. I'm still fighting this flare-up, but I'm sure I can tough it out until time for the surgery."

"About your surgery. Ellen, Dan and I will be arriving on November 9th, the afternoon before your 'grand opening.' Where should we plan to stay when we come up there?"

Mark's question caught me off guard. This was the first I had heard of their intentions. I had not planned to have people come be with me—not even my sister and brothers. Old dogs aren't used to having company under the porch. I tried to talk him out of the notion.

"Mark, I don't expect you all to come all the way to Cleveland. You have your own jobs and families and obligations to attend to. Thanks for offering, but we will be fine."

Mark's response was classic—simple, to the point and definitive.

"Phil, *you* are our family. And besides, we're not asking your permission," he said flatly.

So Susan and I ate, expecting to be joined by the three of them the next afternoon. I must admit, I was anxious for them to get there after all.

November 9th, 2000, dawned gray and cold in Cleveland. As expected, I had made a number of "midnight dashes" to allow my colon to rid itself of the remnants of the wonderful Italian cuisine I had devoured the night before.

After a late breakfast of toast and water, we made preparations for the day ahead. Shortly before 1:30 p.m. I once again found myself on the eleventh floor of the Cleveland Clinic's Crile Building—the Colorectal Surgery Department—for my preoperative testing and consultations. This time Susan was by my side. We had been told to expect all the activities to take three hours or more.

As I checked in at the desk, I felt butterflies starting to form in my stomach. It was reminiscent of the day fifteen years earlier when Susan and I had gone to the courthouse to apply for a marriage license. Signing the papers that day drove the point home to me that I would soon be married. As the receptionist provided me my marching orders on this day, I began to realize that I soon would be gutless.

For the balance of the afternoon we traveled floor to floor, station to station, fulfilling my preoperative obligations—lab work and paperwork, questions asked and answers offered, insurance cards and reassuring smiles.

To my surprise and delight, the process proved extremely efficient and stayed on schedule. There was little idle time. As a result, my mind stayed occupied on the tasks at hand instead of on the surgery to come. Finally, we had one stop left.

"Mr. Van Hooser, Dr. Lavery will see you now."

At this pronouncement Susan and I abandoned our seats. We followed the nurse to the same examination room I had occupied two months earlier. After more questions, answers and forms, the nurse welcomed one of her professional counterparts into the room.

"Mr. Van Hooser, please meet our resident tattoo artist. She's here to work her magic on you."

I knew why she was there. I had been told earlier that the exact location of my stoma (the opening in the abdominal wall through which my body wastes would soon be emptying into my new external appliance) would be determined prior to surgery. A small, but definitive, tattoo was used to mark the location for the surgeon.

I suspected the nurse's levity was an attempt to lighten the overall mood somewhat—to temporarily deflect my attention from the full gravity of what would soon be taking place. It came at a good time. I was ready to play.

"It's good to see you," I said cheerfully. "I'd like to request a tattoo of one of those hula girls that wiggles when your belly flops around. What do you think?"

As I spoke Susan, standing beside me, rolled her eyes and gently began shaking her head back and forth. Her body language seemed intended to say to the nurse, "I hope you have better luck keeping him straight than I have."

The nurse simply smiled toward Susan and said, "I think we've got a live one on our hands."

My response, "That's right. Let's see if we can keep it that way over the next few days."

We all laughed.

The nurse quickly went about her business and located the desired spot. She settled on an area just below my waistline, approximately two or three inches to the right of my belly button. As she was just finishing the application of the tattoo, the examination room door opened. In walked a familiar face. It belonged to Dr. Lavery. This time his entourage was one solitary soul. As before, he wasted little time.

"Hello, Phil," he said, as he negotiated his way through the crowded room to shake my hand. The crush was too imposing for the intern. He stayed near the door. "It's good to see you. You look well." Then turning his attention to Susan he said, "And you must be Mrs. Van Hooser. I'm Dr. Lavery. I'm pleased to meet you."

Susan returned the greeting.

"Well, Phil, are you ready for tomorrow?" Dr. Lavery asked.

"I'm ready to get it over with."

"How have you been feeling? Any problems lately?"

"Just more of the same. Nothing out of the ordinary."

"Well, that's a good thing. At this point in the process, we don't want any surprises." He pulled up a chair and sat down before continuing. "I probably won't see you before the surgery tomorrow. Things will be pretty hectic in the morning. So let me tell you and Mrs. Van Hooser some of what you can expect once things get under way.

"First, and most important. From now until after the surgery, you should not ingest anything but clear liquids. You might want to enjoy a nice cup of chicken broth for dinner this evening. Before you leave the office today, I will give you a prescription for a ***bowel preparation***. Follow the directions to the letter. You don't want to do anything that might risk canceling the surgery at this point. Begin the prep early this evening, then retire early enough to get a good night's sleep. Remember, absolutely nothing by mouth—not even a sip of water—from the time you go to bed until after the surgery. Do you understand so far?"

"Perfectly," I said.

"Good. Tomorrow morning you are scheduled to check in at the surgical unit at 6:00 a.m. That is approximately two hours before your surgery is scheduled to begin. Don't be surprised if it turns out to be somewhat later than that. Things can get backed up in surgery pretty easily.

"Once you arrive, they will get you dressed for surgery and then administer a sedative to help you relax. The sedative will probably make you sleepy." Dr. Lavery turned his attention to Susan and continued, “That’s when we will move your husband to the operating room suite to await his turn. We will then ask you and any other family members or friends to go to the Surgical Waiting Area. Once the procedure has been completed I will contact you by phone there.”

Dr. Lavery’s attention returned to me.

“If all goes well, and we certainly expect that it will, from the time you enter the operating room until we are finished it will be about three to three and a half hours. Upon completion of the surgery, you will be sent to the ***Post-Anesthesia Care Unit*** where they will monitor your vital signs until you are awake. When you are alert and comfortable, you will be moved into a room.”

Dr. Lavery,” I interrupted, “about the room. I would like to request a private room if possible. I have a number of very loud family members that will be visiting me.”

Dr. Lavery just smiled.

“Well, you can request a private room, but it really does no good, unfortunately. They will place you in whatever room is available following the surgery. We will just have to wait and see how good your luck is. Any other questions?”

“No, you all have done a good job of letting us know what to expect,” I said. “I already know more than I really care to.”

Dr. Lavery just smiled and said, “Don’t worry. We are going to take good care of you. And by this time tomorrow you will be known as the patient who formerly suffered from ulcerative colitis. You will be cured.”

With a reassuring smile and a handshake, Dr. Lavery disappeared out the door and down the maze of corridors.

With my brand new belly tattoo and my ***GoLYTELY*** (***Colyte***) prescription in hand, Susan and I were free to go. As we walked through the door back into the waiting area, I got one of my biggest surprises ever. There standing before me, wearing huge "gotcha" grins, were my Pastor, Ed Johnson, and my dear friend and Bible study class member, John Alvarez. They had flown from Florida to be with me. I was stunned.

We embraced warmly. Both were very proud of their successful clandestine efforts. I was proud to see them. Susan just smiled knowingly.

By the time we arrived back at the Guesthouse, our on-campus hotel, my siblings, Mark, Ellen and Dan, were just checking in. But there, with them, was yet another surprise. Anthony Stallins, my high school buddy, just stood there grinning at me. I was overwhelmed. It was wonderful to see them all. My spirits soared.

I have always enjoyed taking good people I know and mixing them with other good people I know. It's great fun to watch the interactions and relationships develop. Now, here before me stood some of the best people I had ever had the privilege of knowing—family, an old friend, two newer friends and my partner for life.

That night the attitude was nothing short of festive. The eight of us broke bread together in the hotel's institutional restaurant and enjoyed each other's company. Well, to be exact, I actually sipped chicken broth while they broke bread together. But we still enjoyed each other's company.

Later we retired to one small hotel room. There, eight of my favorite human beings lounged on the floor, sprawled across beds, leaned against walls—all laughing uproariously for hours at one story after another. My involvement was limited. I was able to participate in about half of every other story.

You see, by then the GoLYTELY had kicked in and was working marvelously, thank you very much. But as I sat straddling that porcelain throne preparing my bowel for its "coming out party" the next morning, I could clearly hear the joy and the rolls of laughter coming from my family and friends. The scene was one of stark contrast to those lonely, frightening nights on the toilet I recalled so vividly just over a year and a half earlier when my illness was on the verge of discovery.

Where there was ignorance, now there was information. Where there was loneliness, now there was camaraderie. Where there was desperation, now there was hope. Where there was fear, now there was a future.

My prayer that night was easy.

"Lord, thank you for the gift of companionship. Thank you for family and friends who love me when we are together and thank you for family and friends who love me when we are apart. Forgive me for not being more open and available to them. May I never allow it to happen again.

Lord, thank you for leading me through the shadows of the past eighteen months. And thank you for the hope that tomorrow brings. I know with you all things are possible and now I know my life is easier with a little help from my friends. I thank you for family, friends and the future. I realize all are gifts from you."

9

The King and I

Friday, November 10, 2000.

As my eyes slowly opened, the quiet stillness of our hotel room enveloped me. As I awoke, semi-consciousness found me in my favored sleeping position—lying on my right side, on the side of the bed offering the easiest, most direct access to the bathroom.

From where I lay, the room's digital alarm clock sat mere inches from my face. Yet, despite the proximity, I still struggled to read its numeric display. Finally, after several seconds of repeated blinking and squinting, the numbers came into focus—4:19 a.m.

I am a morning person. I have been for as long as I can remember. Sleeping late has always been a somewhat contemptuous concept to me. It is hard for me to understand why someone would voluntarily opt to sleep unnecessary chunks of his precious life away when he could be doing something else—anything else—with that time. Personally, I view the activity of sleeping as an obligation. It's something I must do, at a minimal level, to maintain acceptable health and mental acuity.

Even during the prolonged months of sleeplessness and midnight bathroom excursions that my deteriorating condition had wrought, I maintained my personal habit of rising at five each morning. By five-fifteen most of those mornings, I could be found jogging three to four miles at the local park. I liked to run early, on an empty stomach, before my rumbling, grumbling gut became fully involved. As difficult and uncomfortable as those pre-sunrise runs were, I drew inner strength from the mental discipline and sacrifice that defined them.

So it came as little surprise that I was now awake a full eleven minutes before the alarm was programmed to sound and forty-one minutes earlier than normal. It was obvious to me. My mind and body knew something was different about this morning.

I rolled over and turned off the clock's alarm.

For a minute or two before slipping out of bed and heading for the shower, I lay perfectly still, taking note of my surroundings. Though the curtains in our room had been drawn before we retired, I now noticed a sliver of yellow light sneaking through a tiny opening at the point where the drapes were supposed to be joined. It was much too early for the November sun to be up, so I concluded that the light I saw originated from a security light in the parking lot below. Still, it was enough to dimly illuminate various objects in the room.

From where I lay, I could see the accumulated gifts and packages that had been presented to me the evening before. It was an interesting collection.

A couple of fruit and gift baskets sat next to a stack of books and magazines. On top of the literature was a handful of greeting cards, most of them humorous in nature, hand delivered by my visitors on behalf of a variety of friends back in Kentucky and Florida. A "care package," overflowing with foods rich in "comfort" if not nutrition, contained cookies, peanut butter and cheddar cheese crackers, chips, nuts, candies, mints and chewing gum of all kinds.

In the midst of them all sat my favorite gift, courtesy of my thirty-two year old "baby brother" Dan.

The night before, in the midst of all the revelry, Dan had presented me an odd-shaped cardboard box devoid of any bows or wrapping paper. The box had been secured with reinforced packing tape, which required a pocketknife to open. Dan assured me the gift was chosen especially for me during a recent trip through Wyoming and Montana. As I cut and sliced my way into the package, the entire group stood watching and grinning. They already knew its contents. Inside the box was my very own mounted jackalope.

For the uninitiated, a jackalope is a creature whose habitat is limited primarily to cheesy tourist traps and truck stop gift shops throughout the western United States. In such environments, the unsuspecting "tenderfeet from back East" encounter a creature best described as a cross between a jackrabbit and an antelope—a jackrabbit with horns.

For years merchants and locals throughout the Rocky Mountain states and beyond have regaled naïve, gullible, road-weary vacationers with stories of "herds of jackalopes" rampaging through the area. They encouraged motorists to maintain a constant vigil in hopes of being one of the lucky few to spot one of these elusive animals as they race across the barren prairie.

However, on the off chance that visitors don't happen to spot one of these magnificent creatures in the wild, the merchant "just happens to have a young one mounted and on display in the store." And if the traveler shows the slightest bit of interest, the merchant, at "great personal sacrifice," will volunteer to relinquish this "one of a kind" artifact—for a mere $19.95 plus tax, of course.

I have always marveled at the ingenuity and imagination of entrepreneurs. Now I was the proud owner of one of their unique creations—a piece of true Americana. It wasn't the traditional potted plant or the more trendy balloon-a-gram that most hospital patients receive. Instead, this jackalope was absolutely the most creative, off-the-wall gift imaginable. It was perfect for this occasion and this patient. I loved it!

As I glanced across the hotel room, this furry, horned rodent stared back at me with black marble eyes. I relived the moment, several hours before, when it had been presented to me. The recent memory of the amazement, laughter and joy that the occasion elicited caused a smile to crease my face.

Not a bad way to start a morning—especially this morning.

I eased out of bed and made my way to the bathroom. I closed the door and flipped on the light. At that moment the room was bathed in painful illumination. As my eyes adjusted, I stood for a long time examining my reflection while evaluating my current mental state.

So, Phil, how are you doing this morning? Physically, I feel remarkably good. I slept well—much better than I expected. Sleep came quickly and, thankfully, I slept through the entire night. I didn't have to get up. Not even once. Of course, there was really nothing to get up for. My colon was totally empty. The GoLYTELY saw to that last night.

I'm hungry. But I can't eat. They warned me. Nothing—absolutely nothing—by mouth before the surgery. Nothing to eat. Nothing to drink. They were even hesitant when I asked if I could at least brush my teeth. They finally agreed, as long as I promised not to swallow any of the water or toothpaste when I was washing my mouth out. They seemed awfully serious. I'd better keep my promise.

Okay, the day has finally arrived. Am I ready for this surgery? I'd better be. It won't be long now. It's scheduled to start in about two and a half hours. I'll be going under just about the time the kids will be going to school. By the time they get home from school, I will be different.

Before this day is over, I will be split wide open. Before this day is over, I will be gutless. Before this day is over, I will be wearing a bag. Am I ready for all that? Can I handle it?

I think so...I really do.

No, I know so! I have to. I have no choice. I'm out of options.

There's one thing I know for sure. I can honestly say that I've done all that I knew to do. I've made every effort to do whatever the doctors told me. I tried to be a model patient. I feel as if I've had the best treatment and medical advice available. I don't know what else Dr. Morgan and Dr. Truesdale could have done for me. They did everything they knew to do.

Now it's all up to Dr. Lavery and his team. He seems more than competent—they all do. I feel good about him. I feel good about where I am.

The worst thing I could do now is stand here and get myself anxious and all worked up. Nothing good can come out of that.

I need to be emotionally ready—in control—when I come out of this bathroom. Susan will be watching me—reading me. To some degree I suspect she will draw her confidence and comfort levels from me. So will the others. It's been a long time coming, but it's now time to rise to the occasion.

As I engaged in my brief period of self-talk, I began to feel energized. I was at this place—at this time—because I had chosen it. This surgery was not of someone else's choosing. It had not been forced upon me. I was here because I believed I needed to be here. I believed I would be better because of it.

As my mind shifted back to the matter of hygiene, I instinctively reached for my razor and shaving cream. Suddenly I remembered that someone—I couldn't remember who—had cautioned me not to apply any shaving lotion or deodorant on the day of the surgery. For the life of me, I couldn't remember why. Nevertheless, I decided that having a smooth face was the least of my current worries. After all, before the day was out, most of my belly and private parts would be clean-shaven—slick as the proverbial baby's butt. I decided to leave whatever shaving must be done to the surgical prep staff.

I showered quickly. The hot water felt good, but I didn't linger long. I had things to do. I climbed out of the shower, toweled off and climbed into a pair of sweat pants and a T-shirt. I had no intention of trying to impress anyone this morning. "Dress for success" was the furthest thing from my mind. I had decided comfort was the order of the day.

When I exited the bathroom, it was about 4:45 a.m. As I

expected, Susan was up and moving around. She watched me closely, her eyes searching for whatever telltale signs my face or body language might offer.

"Good morning. How you doing?" she asked softly, but cheerfully.

For no good reason, other than it just popped into my head, I immediately launched into my best impromptu, white-middle-aged-men-have-absolutely-no-rhythm rendition of James Brown's signature song.

"I feel good, do-do-do-do-do-do-do. Like I knew that I would now, do-do-do-do-do-do-do…" I half sang, half wailed. Somewhere, I'm sure the self-proclaimed "Godfather of Soul" was writhing more than usual and for a different reason.

Susan looked a bit shell-shocked.

Maybe it was the hour of the morning. Maybe it was the ordeal that lay immediately before us. Maybe it was the appearance of gallows humor at work. Whatever it was, I don't think Susan was quite prepared for it and the melody it rode in on. But she recovered nicely.

She smiled as she shook her head slightly.

"While they're in there, maybe they can perform a talent-ectomy, too," she offered sarcastically.

It was the perfect comeback. I feigned pain. Susan headed for the shower.

By the time Susan emerged from the bathroom about thirty minutes later, I was anxious to get going. The waiting was beginning to be a little monotonous.

We had been instructed to check in at the surgical center at 6:00

a.m. in preparation for my scheduled 8:00 a.m. surgery. I had checked with the hotel desk clerk and had been informed that a shuttle bus stopped in front of the hotel every fifteen minutes, beginning at 4:30 a.m. Its purpose was to offer complimentary guest transportation to various parts of the extensive Cleveland Clinic campus. I had decided Susan and I needed to be on the 5:30 a.m. bus. The rest of my visitors were planning to come later.

By the time Susan had finished dressing, my self-imposed 5:30 a.m. deadline was looming. We hurried to the elevator that carried us to the lobby. Just as we exited the elevator, I saw the shuttle bus pull slowly away from the front of the hotel. My first instinct was to run and flag it down. Just then one of the bellhops intervened.

"Excuse me, sir, but I suggest you don't worry about that one. Just relax. It's cold out there. Stay in here where it's warm. There will be another shuttle along shortly."

I stopped and stood right where I was.

He's right. Why should I be rushing around? There's no good reason to get all worked up and stressed out unnecessarily. After all, they can't start without me, now can they?

"You're right," I said addressing the bellhop. "It's really not worth the effort. Thanks," I offered sincerely.

He smiled and nodded.

Susan took the opportunity to ask where the nearest coffeepot was. The bellhop informed her that the hotel restaurant had just opened. Susan quickly disappeared down the hallway in search of her first cup of coffee in preparation for what promised to be a long day.

Just as Susan stepped away for her caffeine fix, the second elevator's doors slid open. I turned just in time to see my buddy, Anthony Stallins, stepping out.

"There you are," he said, as he hustled toward me.

"Yep, you just caught us. We were a little too late for the five-thirty shuttle. Susan just went looking for coffee. Do you need some?"

"Yeah, but I'll get a cup in a minute," he said, before becoming noticeably more serious. "Phil, I really came down here looking for you. I'm glad I caught you before you got away. How you doing this morning?"

This time I didn't sing.

"I'm good," I answered quickly.

"Are you really?" Anthony pressed.

I could tell by his tone of voice and the seriousness etched in his face that he was genuinely concerned about my emotional welfare and me.

"Anthony, believe me, I really am doing good. I got a good night's sleep. Now I'm ready to get this thing over with. I'm really tired of feeling bad. I'm ready to feel good again."

I looked deep into Anthony's eyes as I spoke. Though he had less hair and more wrinkles than he did when I first met him in elementary school thirty years earlier, the eyes were the same. They were friendly eyes. Compassionate eyes. Honest eyes.

Suddenly, I got the distinct feeling that Stallins had traveled more than one thousand miles one way to be with me for this one isolated moment. He reached out and put his hand on my shoulder. About that time Susan returned. Anthony immediately reached out to her and pulled her in close to us.

"Phil, I want you to know that I came up here because I felt like I needed to. You have been on my mind a lot lately. I want you to know that I love you as a friend and as a brother. I hope you know that."

The sincerity of his words and the heartfelt compassion with which they were offered immediately warmed me. His touch reassured me that he was with me in this moment, in every way. Yet, I could distinctly sense that he was concerned that I might be afraid. I wasn't, but how could I make him know that?

"Anthony, thank you. You will probably never know how much this has already meant to me to have you here for me—and for Susan. I am more convinced than ever that old friends are the best friends. And you are one of my very best."

"I am also convinced that the surgery will go well and that I will be telling the story of this adventure to my kids and grandkids for many years to come. And you can be certain they will know how glad I was that you were here with me."

"However, if for some reason things go wrong today and I don't make it through this surgery, I want you to hear it from me—if the Lord wants me, I'm ready to go. I have no fear, just faith."

As I spoke, I noticed tears forming in Anthony's eyes.

"Can I pray with you before you go?" he asked.

"I wish you would," I replied.

Right there in the middle of the lobby, in the presence of bellhops and desk clerks, the three of us joined arms and hearts and prayed. Anthony offered one of the sweetest, most touching prayers I had ever heard. He acknowledged as a blessing the friendship the two of us have shared over the years. He prayed for a continuation of that blessing and that we would have many more opportunities to spend time together. He prayed for strength and courage for me, Susan and the kids, and he prayed for a successful operation and a complete and uncomplicated recovery.

With a resounding "Amen," Anthony embraced me as a brother, not merely as a friend.

About that time, the shuttle pulled up in front of the hotel.

"Go get a cup of coffee," I said to Anthony. "Susan and I have a little business to attend to. I'll see you this afternoon. You are planning to be at my 'coming out' party aren't you?" I asked with a smile.

"I wouldn't miss it," Anthony replied.

We left Anthony smiling, as we stepped from the lobby into the cold morning darkness and onto the shuttle bus for the short ride to my destiny.

Just a couple of minutes later we arrived at the surgical center, still more than ten minutes early. The waiting room was virtually deserted. I walked up to the desk and announced my name.

"Mr. Van Hooser, we have been expecting you. I'll let them know you are here. In just a moment someone will be right around to take you back and get you started."

Sure enough, after a brief wait, the attendant approached.

"Mr. Van Hooser, will you come with me?"

"Sure. Is it okay for my wife to come along, too?"

"Absolutely. Just follow me."

The young man led us through a maze of hallways that would have made a laboratory rat dizzy. Soon enough, we arrived in an area that was a beehive of activity. The attendant handed us off to a very perky RN. She was blonde and about my age. The (young) woman ushered us into a small, private examination room.

Once there I was issued the obligatory hospital gown, asked to remove my wedding band and watch, and instructed to empty my bladder. Susan and the nurse stepped out of the room momentarily while I changed and fulfilled my obligations.

Afterward, they returned to my side, where I passed my belongings off to Susan. I was told to climb onto the gurney where a warm cotton blanket was made available to cover my dignity. Soon my vital signs had been taken and noted.

"Sir, how are you feeling?" the nurse asked.

"Well, I'm a little cold," I admitted. "But the blanket helps."

"Well, that's good," she chuckled. "But I was really referring to your current level of anxiety. Are you feeling very anxious?"

Now what in the world do I have to feel anxious about? I'm minutes away from major surgery, I'm as close to being naked in public without being arrested as I can be. On top of all that, I'm freezing my butt off. But this is no time for sarcasm.

"Well, I can't say that I feel like I'm on vacation or anything like that. But I feel like I'm doing all right under the circumstances."

"That's good to hear," she offered professionally. "Nevertheless, I'm going to give you an injection of a sedative. In just a few minutes you will become very relaxed. You may even get a little drowsy. That's okay. It will be about fifteen or twenty minutes before we can take you down to PreCare. Your wife can stay with you in the meantime. Okay?"

"You're the boss," I said.

"Ooh, I like the sound of that," she said, as she injected the dose of joy juice before leaving Susan and me to ourselves.

Susan stepped to my bedside and took my hand.

"In case you drop off to sleep, I want you to know that I will be here waiting for you when you wake up. Okay?"

"I know you will. In the meantime, don't have too much fun in the waiting room today with the gang. I feel like I'm missing out on a party."

"Who are you trying to kid? As usual, you *are* the party," she said teasingly.

"Yeah, right," I mumbled. "Susan, while I still know what I'm saying, I want you to know how much I love you and the kids. And I want you to know that if I have to go through this, I'm glad I have you going through it with me."

Susan affirmed my statement by bending down and giving me a gentle, reassuring kiss—much the same kind of kiss that I had seen her administer to our young children hundreds of times before. Soon the sedative—or the kiss—began to take effect.

The nurse returned and told us that the folks from PreCare had called and that an orderly would be by shortly to get me. About that time, the door burst open and in walked Ellen, Mark and Dan. They were a welcome sight.

"Hey, Phil, we're going to get some breakfast. Do you want to come?" Mark asked mockingly.

I laughed. "I'd love to, but there's a little gathering that requires my attendance. How about if you come have supper with me?"

"Count me out," Dan said, jumping into the action. "I hate applesauce."

During this loose period of give and take, a young man pulled back the curtain to my room and entered.

"Good morning, Mr. Van Hooser. I hate to interrupt this party, but it's time for you to go for a little ride. But first I need to check you out," he said.

The young man took my left arm and gently raised it to get a better vantage point from which to read the identification bracelet wrapped around my wrist. Satisfied with what he read, he looked up and said simply, "Yep, it's you. You ready?"

"I'm ready. They were leaving anyway. They're going to breakfast without me."

"Maybe they can take me instead," he said with a chuckle as he reached to release the wheel locks on the bed. Almost immediately, my bed became totally mobile and began to move under the attendant's guidance. I turned my attention back to Susan and my siblings.

"Well, guys, I'll see all of you a little later," I said, as I offered my best parting "parade wave."

"Do good." "See you later." "We love you," were the chorus of replies, accompanied by big, reassuring smiles all around.

I was lost in thought as the young man wheeled me away from my family and toward the operating room suite. As we rolled along, he spoke up.

"Those folks seemed nice. They your family?" he asked.

"Yeah. My wife, sister and two brothers."

"Woo. Your brothers are big ol' boys. I'll bet you could tell some stories on them."

"You'd win that bet," I replied. "But I don't tell many."

"Why not?" the orderly asked.

“Because they know too many on me!”

We both chuckled and kept rolling down one corridor after another.

“Well, they all seem real nice,” he continued. “You’re a lucky man to have family that cares enough to get up this early to come be with you.”

“You got that right,” I said.

But I knew it was more than luck. It was love.

After what seemed to be two or three minutes travel time, we passed through double doors marked:

No Admittance
Authorized Personnel Only

Once inside, I was wheeled past two or three occupied operating rooms to PreCare, a staging area for upcoming operations. I counted five occupied beds in the room. I made number six.

My orderly exchanged pleasantries and paperwork with the attending nurse. With their documentation complete, the orderly returned briefly to my side and patted me on the shoulder.

“I gotta go. It was nice talking to you. I sure hope everything goes well for you.”

I thanked him and he walked away.

As I began to look around at my temporary roommates, my imagination ran wild as I considered what their ailments might be. Of course, I would never know for sure.

One was an elderly lady who was either asleep or unconscious, I couldn’t tell which. Another man lay shifting nervously in his bed from his left side to his right and then back again. A twenty-something-year-old girl was across the room sobbing softly to herself. The others I couldn't see very well.

As I looked around, the nurse-in-charge approached.

"Phillip Van Hooser, right?" she asked coolly.

"Yes?"

"I need to go ahead and start an ***IV*** on you," she said, as she began poking my arm in search of a vein. "But I'll tell you now, everything is backed up in the ***O.R***. due to an earlier emergency. It will probably be at least another hour or so before they call for you. Until then, you can call me if you need me. But as you can see, you're not the only one in here. I've got several others to attend to."

I get the message. Don't be a whiner. Don't be a problem.

I glanced across the room at a clock hanging from the wall. 6:51 a.m.

That's not too bad. They said we would probably start around 8:00 a.m. It looks to me as if they are right on schedule.

"I understand how busy you are. I'll be right here if you need me to help," I said lightly.

No response. No chuckle, no smile, not even a pleasant nod.

This could be a long hour.

About that time, she struck oil. I flinched as the IV needle found its mark and then again as the surgical tape she used to secure it pulled at the hair on my arm. As soon as the IV was flowing properly, she was gone with hardly another word spoken.

As I became still in my bed, I realized the sedative I had been given earlier was still working. My eyelids became heavy. I decided to rest my eyes for just a moment. Soon I was in a deep sleep.

I opened my eyes after my little nap and spent the first few waking seconds trying to remember where I was. It didn't take long. Soon it all came rushing back to me. As I glanced around the room, I immediately noticed four of my roommates were nowhere in sight. Just two of us remained. I didn't attempt conversation.

Next, I looked at the clock on the wall—9:45 a.m. I was amazed. I had been asleep for almost three hours.

As I began stirring in my bed, the nurse reappeared. I didn't expect any warm-fuzzies from her.

"How are you doing?" she asked.

"Okay," I replied simply. "Any idea how much longer?"

"There's really no way of knowing."

Her words seemed tinged with a bit more compassion.

"They are experiencing some challenges they didn't anticipate. It may be another hour or more. In the meantime, would you like to watch some TV?"

"Yeah, sure," I said.

She took a remote and pointed it at a television set suspended from the ceiling.

"Tell me when to stop," she said, as she ran through the channels.

I wasn't used to having someone else in control of the remote, so at the first flickering images of a movie, I spoke up.

"Stop."

I immediately recognized the film. I had seen it many times before. It was *The Dirty Dozen*, starring Lee Marvin and Charles Bronson.

Nothing like a good old "blood and guts" war movie to get one's mind right for surgery.

For almost two hours I watched. With each passing hour I felt myself becoming more impatient.

When the movie ended, I called the nurse over. I now was the only one remaining in the PreCare section.

"I need to go to the bathroom," I said.

She looked over her shoulder as if checking to see if anyone was watching.

"Come on," she said. "I'm going to let you walk to the bathroom. You've been lying there long enough."

With that she helped me out of the bed and walked beside me, driving the IV stand, to the bathroom just across the hall. It felt good to let the blood flow back down into my legs and feet. I went into the john. She stood guard at the door, waiting for me to reemerge.

"What's taking so long?" I asked as we walked back toward my bed.

"I'm not really sure."

"Well, has anyone told my wife that I'm not in surgery yet? She may be concerned."

"She knows. We've kept her informed. But she might like to hear from you. Would you like to call her?" she asked, with the most compassion I had seen her exhibit.

"Yes, I would."

The nurse wheeled my bed across the room to the nearest telephone, punched a few numbers and handed the receiver to me. Soon I was talking to Susan. It was good to hear her voice. She sounded upbeat.

While we were talking, word came that they were ready for me in the OR. I hung up and almost immediately was wheeled back down the hall and into a cool, brightly-lit room. Once there the ***anesthesia*** team, all working behind surgical masks, took over.

"Sir, could you tell us your name?"

"Phillip Van Hooser."

"What are you in for?"

"Don't you know?" I asked, half-kidding, half-serious.

"Yes, sir, we know. But we ask anyway as part of our proper patient identification program. It's a safeguard. It's our policy."

The response made me feel better.

"And a good one it is. I'm here to have my colon removed."

"Well, what a coincidence. We're here to take your colon from you. On top of that, we're going to take good care of you," one said as she worked. "Mr. Van Hooser, I'm starting the anesthesia in your IV now. It will take effect shortly. Where do you live?"

"Ocala, Florida."

"My, my, you're a long way from home. But it sounds like a great place to live. Is it warm down there?"

"It's beautiful."

"What do you do down there?"

"I'm a professional speaker and author."

"Really? What books have you written?"

By this time I had to concentrate hard on the questions I was being asked and the answers I offered. I could tell I was beginning to drift away. The last words I remember speaking before floating off into Never-Never Land were these:

"The name of the book is *You're Joe's Boy, Ain't Ya?* And you can order your own copy from Amazon.com."

As I spoke the words, I remember thinking helplessly, *Will my last words really be a commercial?*

I learned later that my surgery lasted from 12:30 p.m. until 3:10 p.m. I was in the Post Anesthesia Care Unit (PACU) for another two and a half-hours where the nurses helped me recover from the immediate effects of the anesthesia.

I remember very little about my time in PACU—nothing but flimsy little confusing tidbits floating around in a dream-like fog.

My conscious thought and memory did not return until almost six hours after the surgery began, almost three hours after it had concluded. I distinctly remember being wheeled into my assigned hospital room. Initially, I recall there wasn't much intense pain. Just general, overall discomfort.

But from my head downward, there were tubes and monitors everywhere. One of the more unpleasant and uncomfortable was the ***nasogastric (NG) tube*** that had been inserted through my nose and down into my stomach. Along with the NG tube, I wore a tube over both ears that pumped pure oxygen up my nose.

As I glanced further down my body, I noticed two IVs where only one had been before. I patted my belly gently and, under my hospital gown, I could feel some sort of tube that had been inserted into the upper regions of my abdomen. I had no idea, and very little interest, in what its purpose was.

I was unable to feel the actual abdominal incision due to the thick sterile dressing that covered it. I could, however, feel the large gauge drainage tube that extended from the lowest section of the incision in my lower pelvic region. On top of that, the attending nurse told me that a ***urinary catheter*** had been inserted during surgery, though I could not feel it. And frankly, I had no desire to do so.

Finally, I knew that there, under my gown somewhere, was my ileostomy—my new bag. I was immediately curious about it. But apparently they were not quite ready to introduce me to it. That would come a little later.

Soon after arriving in the room and after the gauges, monitors and equipment had been inspected, a nurse asked if I felt up to seeing visitors. I answered yes, even though I wasn't quite sure.

The first person to come in was Susan. I must have looked a mess. But she never let on that it was a problem.

Soon Ellen, Mark, Dan and Anthony joined us. I asked about Ed Johnson and John Alvarez and was told that they had stayed at the hospital until the surgery was successfully completed. Only then did they rush back to the airport to catch a Florida flight that would take them home and back to their responsibilities.

I clearly remember everyone's faces. Each exhibited a definite look of concern, though they tried hard to disguise it. All of them wanted to know how I felt. I wanted to know how the surgery went.

"How did it go?" I asked.

"They said it went perfectly. Dr. Lavery told me you did great,"

Susan said.

"That's good," I offered weakly, thankful for the good report.

Someone else spoke up.

"Phil, you're the man!"

"Yeah, I really look like 'the man,' don't I?" I protested.

"Well, you must be. Here you lay in a private room on the VIP floor."

"Huh? What are you talking about?" I asked, still thoroughly confused.

"Phil, you're in a private room right down the hall from some king from one of those middle eastern countries. The whole floor is crawling with security guards and secret service agents. That can only mean one thing. YOU'RE THE MAN!"

I just smiled at the thought.

What a day this has been. I arrived with my personal entourage at the Cleveland Clinic from half way across the country, expecting to have my physical needs attended to by some of the premier healthcare professionals in the world.

Unbeknownst to me, a king has also traveled to the Cleveland Clinic with his entourage from halfway around the world to have his physical needs attended to by those same premier healthcare professionals.

Imagine living in a nation where world class healthcare is available to prince and commoner alike. Only in America could the day begin with a pitiful James Brown impersonator receiving equal time, attention and care as royalty.

Yes, physicians are here. A king is here. And I am here. But I've placed my faith, my confidence and my very future in the hands of the Great Physician—the King of Kings.

10

Left Holding the Bag

From the time I was settled into my hospital room, it seemed as if I was convalescing in the middle of Grand Central Station. In addition to my visitors, a virtual nonstop collection of nurses, technicians, dieticians, orderlies, janitors and volunteers of all sorts paraded in and out. There was blood to be drawn, temperature to be taken, medication to be modified, IV solution to be replenished, bodily fluids to be disposed of and dressings to be changed.

Please don't get me wrong. To a person, regardless of the shift or area of responsibility, the individuals I encountered were the most attentive, helpful, caring and professional I had ever witnessed. If I so much as wiggled or groaned, they were there to attend to my every need. I appreciated that. Though my personal experience with professional caregivers was admittedly limited, I considered these to be some of the best.

Yet, as they provided near-constant attention to my health and physical needs, my focus never drifted far from my two greatest concerns—the pain and the bag.

It's strange. I can't see the pain. No one can. But I know it's there. Hidden from human view beneath a covering of flesh and bravado.

I can't see the bag either. But it's down there—somewhere—buried beneath blankets, sheets and a hospital gown.

Both of these are real. Nothing has ever been more real to me. The pain and the bag hang over me like some dark, threatening cloud. A cloud that requires constant attention—and concern. Will it float harmlessly past or will it unleash even more devastation and suffering?

Is there more pain to come? I have been able to endure the physical pain to this point. But it's getting worse. I know it. I can feel it. How much worse can it get? How much more can I stand?

What about the emotional and psychological pain of wearing a bag—of being different? My family and friends will know and they'll still love me. But soon, others will know. They will whisper. They will look. They will wonder. Can I handle it? Am I prepared to be different? Am I strong enough to be different?

It's good to be loved and attended to by family, friends and professional caregivers, but what I need most right now is peace and rest. Peace for the mind and rest for the body.

As the evening wore on, my physical pain intensified. What I described as "general discomfort" in the first few hours after surgery was quickly becoming "serious suffering."

I must admit I had been told to expect this. Dr. Lavery had warned me early on that the initial recuperation period with this particular surgery was "quite painful." But somehow I never took the time to give it much thought.

Maybe it was the disarming lilt in his New Zealand accent that stole some of the impact from his initial warning. Maybe I fancied myself as having an "above average" pain threshold—I was simply "tougher" than the average patient. Maybe I was subconsciously trying to measure up to my childhood memory of the heroics surrounding my sister's varicose veins or my brother's cut lip. Then again, maybe it was an unholy alliance of all three. Whatever it was, as the evening wore on I began to focus more and more on the physical pain.

During their frequent bedside checks the nurses were fond of asking, "Mr. Van Hooser, how are you feeling?" My initial response during the first several hours was, "Fine. Just tired." My answer seemed to satisfy them.

Eventually, though, the nurses appeared to become more wary of my standard answer. Their questions became more probing.

"Mr. Van Hooser, how are you doing?"

"Fine, I guess."

"What is your level of pain?"

"It's not too bad."

"Well, on a scale of one to ten, with one being comfortable and ten being terribly uncomfortable, how would you rate the pain you are experiencing now?"

"Oh, about a four or so," I lied.

"Are you sure? Do you need something for the pain? It's available for you."

"No, I'm fine. I'll let you know if it gets worse."

The pain got progressively worse, but I never let them—or my visitors—know. I just gritted my teeth and prepared myself for a long night. In my mind, I was sure the pain would be lessened with the dawning of a new day. Foolishly, I was determined to tough the first night out.

About 10:00 p.m., Susan and the rest of the gang left my bedside to return to their hotel. Honestly, I was glad to see them go.

Don't get me wrong. I was encouraged and my spirits were bolstered by their presence and hands-on concern. Dan was quick to lovingly hound me into regular use of the ***spirometry device***, a breathing apparatus, the nurses had provided.

The molded plastic contraption reminded me of the carnival sideshow where a sledgehammer is swung in hopes of striking a target with enough force to ring a bell aloft. A simple concept. Spectators gawk and cheer. Participants realize the activity is harder than it looks.

This respiratory tool followed the same theme—in reverse. Instead of striking a platform, I inhaled as deeply as possible through a mouthpiece. The volume of air I inhaled caused a small ball in the device's tube to move. Incremental markings on the tube indicated my level of success (or lack thereof). During the process, my spectators would gawk and cheer.

The whole experience was torturous. My lungs didn't appreciate the workout and neither did my recently dissected stomach muscles. But brother Dan was an exacting taskmaster as well as an enthusiastic cheerleader. He understood that deep breathing and coughing were necessary to rid the lungs of any fluids that might have settled there. He was quick to remind me of what he had learned—that such fluids could serve as the breeding ground for post-operative pneumonia.

Ellen and Susan got involved too. Every hour or so, one of them took it upon herself to rub and massage my feet and legs. The nurses had explained that this would help stimulate the circulation and blood flow, thus reducing the chance of blood clots forming in my lower extremities due to temporary inactivity.

Any one of them was always ready to volunteer to rush off in search of a fresh supply of ice chips to help moisten my dry mouth and tongue.

In their own way, each had attended to my every physical need. On that rare occasion when one of my needs was beyond what they could supply, they were quick to flag down a nurse. Through it all, they teased me good-naturedly and engaged me in light conversation. Both helped to occupy my mind, raise my spirits and make the time go by more quickly.

But quite frankly, I had had enough support for one day.

Susan had originally intended to spend the first night with me, but I urged her to leave with the rest of them. Why?

First, all the medical indicators suggested I was responding well. There were no abnormal pulse rates, temperature spikes or blood pressure variations to be concerned about. The nursing staff assured her that everything was under control.

Second, I was dead tired and I desperately needed to rest. Susan did, too. I knew she had been up and going since before 5:00 a.m. We needed to view this recuperation period as a marathon, not a sprint. We needed to pace ourselves to ensure we had fuel left in our tanks for the challenges ahead.

Finally, the most compelling reason was I wanted to be by myself. It had been several hours since the conclusion of my surgery, but still I had not seen the results of Dr. Lavery's handiwork. I figured that before long the ***dressing*** covering my ***incision*** would need to be changed. It was then that I planned to be introduced to my new stoma and the accompanying appliance. But the storm clouds were still hovering. Was I ready?

How will I react to seeing my own exposed intestine? Will it be gruesome? Will it be more than I can take? As a general rule I've always had a strong stomach, but can I handle the magnitude of something this personal?

I've heard and read stories of people who couldn't handle it. They couldn't deal with the psychological issue of wearing an appliance—a bag. Apparently, it had nothing to do with their physical condition. Their stoma worked fine. Yet, accepting and adjusting to it emotionally proved to be a more difficult problem. To adapt, some even required professional counseling. Would I?

I already know of a couple of cases where the psychological impact was so great that instead of just accepting the stoma and moving forward, the wearers opted instead to withdraw into themselves, becoming virtual social recluses. I couldn't stand that. I enjoy people too much.

I really can't imagine that would ever happen to me. But how can I be sure? The only way I will ever know for sure is to get my first look and then get on with it. And I don't want that first look to come while I'm surrounded by my family and friends. Not even Susan. First, I need to deal with this alone.

"Phil, we're going now. Do you need anything?"

Susan's words interrupted my innermost thoughts.

"No, I'm doing fine. I'm gonna try to rest. Don't feel like you have to come too early tomorrow morning. Sleep in. Have a nice breakfast. Just take your time," I told her. "I'm not going anywhere. I'll be here when you get back," I told them all.

Before heading for the door, each came to my bedside. Their smile, wink or gentle pat let me know that though they were leaving for now, they would continue to be there for me. Susan was the last.

"Phil, sweet dreams," she said. "I love you and I'm proud of you." Then she leaned forward and whispered into my ear, "Remember, you don't have ulcerative colitis anymore. Your colon is gone. You're healed. Now all you have to do is get well."

She punctuated her message with a little kiss on my cheek before leaving to join the others in the hall.

Healed. No more colitis. She's right. I hadn't even thought about that. I guess there have been too many tubes, monitors and interruptions to occupy my thoughts.

If I can just get through this night and a few more like it, life will be good again. All this pain and discomfort will be gone. I will be back to normal.

The thought comforted me. As quiet settled over the room, I

closed my eyes, desperate to discover and explore even more comforting thoughts. But as weariness and fatigue soon took their place, I drifted off to sleep.

Throughout the night, about once every thirty to forty-five minutes, the graveyard shift nurses entered my room and roused me. They came to make their checks and do their duties. They worked to be as unobtrusive as possible, hoping I would slip easily back to sleep once their tasks were complete. Several times I did, but it was still a long night.

Shortly after sunrise a new group of nurses arrived to begin their 12-hour shift. A nurse in her mid-50's came into my room to make the first of her many bed checks on me. I was awake. I had been for some time.

"Good morning, Mr. Van Hooser," she said pleasantly as she read my name from her chart. "How are you feeling this morning?"

"About the same as last night," I replied.

"Did you rest well?"

"Not great. I couldn't get comfortable. This tube in my nose was especially aggravating. When do you think it can be removed?" I asked.

"I'll check on that right away and see what we can do for you. But first, let me take a quick look at your incision."

As she spoke, she peeled back the blanket and the sheet that covered me. She folded them back to about my mid-thigh. Before going further, she spoke again.

"Now I'm going to pull your gown back for a minute. Okay?"

Okay? How in the world could I stop you? I'm helpless. I can't sit up. I can't raise my leg. I can barely reach and scratch my nose. Okay? What do you expect me to say? I don't think it really makes much difference if it is okay with me or not.

But wait a minute. It's just the two of us. Here's my opportunity.

"Yeah, that will be fine," I said softly. "But before you do, would you go find a mirror?"

"A mirror?"

My request obviously caught her off guard.

"Yeah, a mirror. I can't sit up or even raise my head enough to get a good look at my belly. It hurts too much. So a mirror would be a big help. I'd like to see what kind of scar there will be. Okay?"

The nurse mustered a confused little smile and shrugged.

"Let me go see what I can find."

In less than five minutes she was back with a mirror in hand.

"I found one," she announced proudly while holding it up for me to see. It was round, about five inches in diameter, mounted in a plastic casing with a handle. I suspected she scavenged it from the ladies' lounge.

"You'll also be happy to know that while I was gone, I checked and it's okay to remove the oxygen and NG tubes. You will feel much better in just a minute."

The nurse laid the mirror on the table beside my bed. Gently she reached across my body and lifted the oxygen tube from under my nose and over my head. She then turned her attention to the NG tube.

This small-gauge, soft plastic tube was a primary source of my discomfort. It was obvious to anyone who entered the room. It extended from my nose, across my chest, over the side of the bed and into a collection bag somewhere below. The tube had been inserted through my nostril and down into my stomach after I was asleep just before surgery. Its purpose was to drain fluids from my stomach. Yet, it had been so long since I had eaten or drunk anything it was hard for me to imagine there was anything left to drain.

"Mr. Van Hooser, I need to pull this tube out. It may prove to be somewhat uncomfortable, but just hang on. It will only take a few seconds."

I learned long ago that "somewhat uncomfortable" from the lips of physicians and nurses actually means "hurts like the devil" in laymen's terms. I braced myself for the inevitable.

Upon request, I leaned my head as far back as possible. She grasped the tube.

"Hold on. You will feel a little tug," she said as she began to withdraw the tube that ran clear to the pit of my stomach. I felt a little tug. The tube began to move.

To my surprise, it really didn't hurt. However, the strange sensation of the tube moving across flesh deep in my throat caused a gag reaction, which in turn caused my body to jerk involuntarily. When it did, unspeakable pain engulfed me. I had momentarily forgotten about my new stomach incision. But the raw, dangling nerve endings reminded me quickly.

"Ummmph," I groaned loudly.

"Mr. Van Hooser, hang on…it's coming…it's almost out…there we go," the nurse said as she retrieved the last of what looked to me to be at least 100 feet of slimy NG tube from my snout.

"How do you feel now?" she asked.

"Oh, great. Never better," I croaked sarcastically as the initial shock wave of abdominal pain began to subside somewhat. But it was an immediate relief to have the tube gone.

The nurse disposed of the tube, allowing me a few seconds to recover. She quickly returned to my side.

"Now if you're ready, we'll see what things look like down here," she said.

Very gently she lifted my gown and draped it back up over my chest, leaving me almost completely exposed. Nothing was left to the imagination. At the moment, I could not have cared less. Besides, her focus was elsewhere. She continued to work, removing the blood-soaked absorbent pad that lay loose on top of the incision.

"Good. Very good," she said as she surveyed the wound. "Everything looks fine to me. Would you still like to take a look?"

"Absolutely," I said, as I drew a long breath in anticipation of the sight.

The nurse reached for the mirror and positioned it about eighteen inches above my midsection and angled it so that I could see the reflection of my belly. The image I saw in the mirror was graphic.

A strip of shaved, slick skin about six inches wide extended from my lower breastbone all the way down to the lower region of my pubic area. The portion of bare belly looked strange in contrast to the thick stand of body hair totally surrounding it. It was the first time since my pre-adolescent days that I had seen even a portion of my stomach hairless.

In the middle of the shaved strip was an incision that began about three or four inches above my belly button and extended straight down to the pubic bone. In total, it measured about 10 to 11 inches in length. It had been closed with sturdy metal staples—there looked to be a dozen or more—instead of the traditional synthetic stitches. As a result of the staples, the closed incision was raised and puckered, creating a prominent ridge of dissected flesh up and down my midsection. In some places the wound actually gaped open a millimeter or two. Dried blood was all along the incision line.

That's not a sight for the weak of heart.

As I encouraged the nurse to gradually reposition the mirror, I noticed at the very bottom of the incision, just above the pubic bone, that another tube jutted forth from somewhere deep in my abdomen.

"Now that's gonna make a doozy of a scar," I said, trying to lighten my own mood. "What's the purpose of that tube down there?"

"That's a ***pelvic drain***. It was inserted during surgery. Those tubes are attached to this small pump at the foot of your bed. The drain is placed in the pelvis because that's where fluids tend to collect after abdominal surgery. The pump draws those fluids out, thereby reducing the possibility of infection."

She bent down for a closer inspection of the fluid collection bag.

"There doesn't seem to be much fluid here. That's a good thing. It probably won't be much longer until they let us remove that drain, too," she said encouragingly.

As she spoke, I felt my pulse begin to accelerate. Though she may not have been prepared for my next request, I knew the time had come for me to ask to see the bag.

"Before you put the mirror away," I said as evenly and unemotionally as possible, "If you don't mind, I would like to see the bag—my bag."

The nurse immediately shot a concerned look my way. She hesitated ever so slightly before responding.

"Have you seen the ***enterostomal therapist*** yet?" she asked quickly.

"I don't believe I have. I don't recognize that title," I replied.

"The enterostomal therapist, or ***E.T.***, as we refer to her, is normally the one responsible for introducing new patients to their stomas and the appliance. She has received special training in dealing with colon surgery patients and those who have received an ileostomy. She is much better prepared to help you in the event you…"

Her voice trailed off but I knew exactly what she was thinking. She thought the E.T. would be better prepared to help me in the event I had psychological trouble accepting the changes my body had undergone.

"Listen, I want you to know this is very important to me. I have given this a lot of thought and I'm ready to see it now. I wasn't ready yesterday and who knows about tomorrow. But I know I'm ready now."

The nurse protested slightly.

"Sir, I just want you to understand that the E.T. is the person who will teach you about caring for your loop ileostomy. She will be able to share all the information you need to know and will be able to answer all your questions before you leave the hospital."

"Fine, I'll save all the hard questions for her. But right now I just want to have a look," I insisted.

After a few seconds of obvious hesitation she finally relented.

"Well, I guess it will be okay," she said more to herself than to me. "But if you get lightheaded…"

"I won't," I interrupted.

With that, the nurse repositioned the mirror slightly over the lower right quadrant of my abdomen. She changed the angle of the looking glass and the first image of my new "temporary loop ileostomy" came into view.

"There!" I blurted out. "Please hold the mirror right there."

For the next minute or so I examined the bag and as best I could, the stoma itself.

The bag or appliance was made from some sort of pliable transparent plastic. It reminded me of one of the plastic freezer bags my wife uses to preserve fruits and vegetables. As I looked more closely, I could see that the back of the bag, the part in contact with my flesh, was not transparent.

The bag itself was not nearly as big and bulky as I had imagined it would be. I estimated that its dimensions were approximately the size of a small bag of popcorn one might buy at a movie theatre.

The shape of the bag was interesting. It resembled an upside down hot water bottle—the kind I had enjoyed snuggling up to on cold winter nights as a child—only much smaller. Instead of having the opening to the bag at the top, it was at the bottom and was designed to serve as a drain from which its contents could be emptied. This "drain" was clamped shut by some sort of sturdy plastic clip, resembling a girl's hair barrette.

The bag was attached to my shaved side at the exact location marked by my tattoo from the day before. It was secured with what appeared to be some sort of bonding agent and extra wide adhesive strips.

The bag was wrinkled and looked deflated as it rested atop my right upper thigh. Upon closer inspection I noticed a small amount of murky liquid that had drained to the bottom of the bag.

"What's that?" I asked the nurse.

"That's waste that has drained from your ***stoma***. That means it's working," she reassured me. "There hasn't been much collected because you haven't started on soft foods yet. When you do, the color, consistency and amount of the waste will be determined by what you have eaten and drunk and in what quantities. What you see here is just some residual liquid and mucous from your small intestine. It's normal."

I asked her to shift the angle of the mirror. As she moved it closer, I got a good look at the stoma itself.

The scarlet red and purple color of the stoma stood in stark contrast to the white shaved belly around it.

"Is it bruised?" I asked innocently.

"No, it's not bruised. It looks very healthy. Its color indicates that the circulation in the bowel is excellent. That's exactly the way we want it to look."

Compared to the delicate and painstaking work—cutting, splicing and stapling—that I understood went into creating the pelvic pouch which I would never see, the loop ileostomy construction looked fairly simple to my untrained eye.

It looked as if a hole had been cut in my side through which someone had fished out a loop of my bowel. The bowel had then been pulled to about one half inch or so past the surface of the skin and somehow attached to the abdominal wall.

Once secured, it seemed that someone had taken a sharp knife and simply cut a small even slit in the bowel, allowing the stream of waste that flowed to that point to spill into the attached bag.

The sight of my exposed bowel was strangely mesmerizing. As I lay staring at it, strange variations of thoughts rushed through my head.

That's my intestine—my guts!

Will I be able to wear jeans over this thing? Will anyone notice?

I wonder if the kids will want to see it. Could they handle the sight of it?

Will this be a turnoff to Susan?

I wonder if you can swim with one of these.

How do you bathe or shower while wearing one of these?

I wonder if it will give off an odor.

I wonder how many people I've met on the street with one of these and I didn't even know it.

I had many questions and concerns. But as I lay in the bed entertaining these and other thoughts, a general feeling of relief began to settle over me. I realized I had come face-to-face with my unknown. A significant personal fear—and I had confronted it head on. The result? A minor psychological victory, but one that prepared me to move forward. I began to feel a new level of confidence that things were going to work out.

After an extended period of examination from several different angles, I freed the nurse from her duties.

"Thanks for letting me take a look. I feel much better now."

She seemed genuinely relieved by my controlled reaction.

That left me with my other major issue to address. I was weak. I was tired. And I was sore. Sore as I had ever been. I've never been hit by a bread truck but I can't imagine it would have hurt any worse than what I was feeling that morning. Anything that caused me to move even one muscle in my midsection was unbelievably agonizing. The only relief came when I lay perfectly still.

About mid-morning Susan and the gang returned. They seemed well rested and in good spirits. With them they brought a new visitor, my good buddy, Jim McDaniel, who had just arrived from Kentucky.

Jim, Anthony and I had run around together for more than twenty-five years.

The group is complete. Here I lay, surrounded on every side by loved ones—my mate, my siblings and my old friends.

Just before noon the head nurse working the floor stopped by for a visit. The entire group was present.

"Mr. Van Hooser, how's your pain?"

By this time I had grown tired of lying and was growing desperate for relief.

"Honestly? I'm hurting a lot," I finally confessed.

"On a scale of one to ten, with…"

I interrupted her before she could go any farther. I knew the drill. I had become familiar with their pain scale.

"I'm at an eight for sure. Maybe a nine," I admitted.

"Have you been using your ***PCA pump***?"

"I don't even know what you're talking about."

The nurse looked at me with amazement. Her hands on her hips added a definite hint of aggravation.

"Are you telling me that you have not taken any pain medication for the past twenty-four hours?"

"I'm almost positive I haven't."

"Mr. Van Hooser, it has been available to you the entire time. This is not the time to try to be a hero," she scolded. "I want you to listen very carefully as I explain something to you."

The others in the room fell silent, along with me as the lecture began.

"Managing your pain is a key element in your overall recovery process. Our goal here is to get you on your feet and walking as soon after surgery as possible. I know that doesn't necessarily excite you right now, but walking is without question the very best thing you can do to accelerate the healing process. The problem is that you are sore and you don't feel like getting up. Am I right?"

"Yes," I admitted meekly.

"Well, if you don't get up and start moving around, the opportunity for all kinds of other medical problems creeps in. That's where the pain medication helps. If we can lessen your pain by way of medication, then you feel better and are more able to get up and move around more quickly. And as I said, the sooner you do that, the sooner you get out of here and the sooner you begin to feel better. Any questions?"

"I think I understand what you're saying. But you asked if I had used the 'PCA Pump.' I remember someone mentioning the term early on, but I never paid much attention. What is it?"

"'PCA' is short for '***Patient-Controlled Analgesia***.' The 'pump' refers to a medication-infusion pump that has been attached to your IV line all along. It's been sitting here, waiting for you to use it ever since they moved you into this room. All you have to do is push this little button and the pump will deliver a dose of pain medication directly to your blood stream when you need it."

"But, I'm no doctor," I said. "How will I know how much medication is too much?"

"There's no need for you to worry about that. Your physician has prescribed a dosage of pain medication based on your weight and the level of discomfort most patients experience after your type of surgery. The dosage is computer-controlled within the pump. You cannot overdose—even if you wanted to. You can hit the pump constantly for the next hour and it will still only deliver a dose of medication every six minutes—no more."

She paused momentarily for effect and looked me right in the eye. Once she knew she had my attention, she drove her point home forcefully.

"Mr. Van Hooser, if you want to get well and go home—use the pump!"

When the nurse finished her pointed explanation, it was clear to me that I had been suffering needlessly for a full day. It was also clear to the others in the room who had been listening. Before I could respond to the nurse, my brother Mark spoke up.

"Ma'am, you don't have to worry about the pain medication issue any more. I'm driving now," he said as he reached over and took control of the PCA Pump's button.

For the next two days Mark became my self-appointed "pain medication administrator." I quickly learned there was no need for me to concern myself at all. Every six or seven minutes, regardless of what was happening around me, I heard the telltale "click" reminding me that Mark was on the job. And it worked.

Though still terribly uncomfortable, with the help of Mark and the trusty PCA Pump, I soon reverted to the "tolerable" pain level. As a result, later that very day I was up and walking—gingerly—the halls of the Cleveland Clinic.

Over the next two days I was upgraded to a soft diet to which my system responded nicely. The nurses assured me that my stoma was working perfectly.

Meanwhile Mark, Dan, Anthony, Jim, Ellen and Susan took turns accompanying me as I wandered the corridors. I was gradually getting better day by day. Eventually, I progressed to the point that Dr.

Lavery informed me that I would be released from the hospital on Tuesday morning, just four days after the initial surgery. But first I had to be cleared by the enterostomal therapist (E.T).

The morning of my scheduled discharge, the E.T. came to my hospital room and provided a private lesson for Susan and me on the proper care of my new ileostomy. Though I'm sure she had done this hundreds of times before, still she fielded our every question with remarkable patience and understanding.

"Mr. Van Hooser, I'm sure your last few days here have been challenging. Major surgery always is. Just keep in mind that having a proctocolectomy was a necessary step for you to get better. Now my job is to help you adapt to your new ileostomy for whatever period you may have it."

"Today I am going to teach you how to change your appliance and what to do to ensure proper hygiene for your stoma. What you will learn is not hard, but it is important and it is necessary. Additionally, I will share situations for which you should be on the lookout in an effort to avoid any serious future problems. Are there any questions I can answer before we start?"

"I have a question," Susan said, breaking the ice. "How often will the appliance need to be changed?"

"Temporary appliances, such as Mr. Van Hooser's, should be changed every three or four days. If it were a permanent ileostomy, it would need to be changed weekly. Initially, it may take up to a half-hour to complete. Mr. Van Hooser, once you become more comfortable with the process, that time should be cut in half. I encourage you, Mrs. Van Hooser, to become familiar with the process should your husband need a little assistance from time to time. But remember, this is his responsibility. There's no need to baby him."

Susan and the nurse both cut their eyes at me. I suddenly felt tremendously outnumbered. In an effort to change the subject slightly, I asked a question of my own.

"When is the best time to change the bag?"

"You may change the appliance any time you wish. But most people find that the best time is first thing in the morning before they eat or drink anything. That is when the gastrointestinal system is primarily inactive. Later in the day after you've eaten, you probably will experience more problems with waste exiting the stoma without the bag in place." She paused for just a few seconds, wrinkled up her nose, smiled and concluded, "It can get a little messy."

Emboldened by her directness and candor, I continued with my questions.

"Is there any way I can control the 'output'?"

"Not really. The whole process is involuntary. If you ingest something, eventually something else is going to be deposited into the appliance as waste. The problem is that you don't know when and how much. It just appears. Of course, the more you eat, the more the output. And keep in mind the appliance will collect gas as well as solids. That's why we caution wearers to be careful about eating foods that tend to be gaseous."

I smiled at the thought of the bag blowing up like a balloon. Though sophomoric, the mental image tickled me somehow.

"Mr. Van Hooser, let me ask you a question. Have you had any difficulty emptying your appliance over the past few days?"

"Really, it's not that hard," I admitted. "They cautioned me to empty it whenever it gets half to three quarters full. I just shuffle into the bathroom and sit down on the toilet. Then I unclip the fastener at the bottom of the bag and dump the contents into the toilet bowl. Before refastening the clip, I clean the bottom of the bag with toilet paper and that's about it."

"Perfect!" she said enthusiastically. "Once you get on a solid diet, you can expect to empty it six to eight times a day—more if you are a really big eater. Now let's get you as comfortable with changing the appliance."

For the next few minutes the nurse led me patiently, step by step, through the entire process. Using a cotton ball, she had me gently rub some sort of solvent around the edges of the adhesive tape which attached the bag to my skin. Slowly and methodically she had me peel more and more of the adhesive back as the solvent worked its magic. Eventually, the adhesive loosened completely.

As I lifted the used bag away from my side, for the first time I got an unobstructed view of my stoma. It was surreal. I remembered in grade school how we had studied about a cow that had a transparent, plexiglass window placed in her side so researchers and observers could watch the actual anatomical performance of one of Bossie's stomachs. Now I was able to do the same but without the window.

Just as the bag was lifted away, a small portion of whiskey-colored liquid waste oozed forth from my stoma. I froze. I didn't know what to do. Sensing my hesitancy, the E.T. reached for a Kleenex and nonchalantly wiped the discharge away—just like that.

"See, Mr. Van Hooser? It's really no big deal. The stoma itself has no nerve endings so you can clean it by contacting it directly."

She then produced a wet cloth and soap and had me wash the area thoroughly. She explained it needed to be washed well to keep infections from forming. Once washed, the area was dried thoroughly, after which a type of powder resembling talc was applied to the area around the stoma. A fresh bag was provided and I was shown how to apply the bonding agent to the adhesive and the adhesive to my skin. As she had predicted, the entire process took about fifteen minutes from start to finish.

"That wasn't too bad, was it?" she asked.

"Not really," I admitted. "I think I have a pretty good teacher."

"Well, thank you. There are just a couple of other things I need to caution you about. First, if you see any blood that has collected in the appliance, please call us. It rarely happens, and when it does, it is usually a minor issue. But we don't want to take any chances."

"Second, for the period from now until you return for your reversal, there are certain foods you would be wise to avoid completely. I will give you a pamphlet with a comprehensive list, but a few examples are popcorn, nuts of all kinds and any foods that are stringy or fibrous in nature. Avoid greasy and spicy foods, onions, raw fruits and vegetables. Such foods are extremely hard to digest and could cause an obstruction. Believe me when I tell you that you don't want an obstruction. I suggest you also cut out carbonated beverages. They produce a lot of gas."

"What can I have?" I asked.

"Mashed potatoes, cooked vegetables, soups, bananas—any soft foods are fine."

"What about meat?"

"Chicken, fish, turkey and lean meats are all fine as long as they are tender. The rule of thumb is that if you can't cut them with a fork—avoid them. Any other questions?"

We had none of any consequence.

Before leaving, the E.T. gave us the various supplies we needed to get started. She also gave us her contact information, wished us luck and was gone. Following her departure, I felt a little like I did the day my wife and I brought our firstborn home from the hospital.

What now? I know what I'm supposed to do. But can I really do it? She must think so. She has abandoned me. I guess there is no turning back now. It's time to solo.

Though I had a few doubts my body was healing, my spirits

were high and my confidence was growing. I was anxious to get out of the hospital and back home. It was time to get on with the next stage of my life.

After four days of near constant attention, I was discharged from the Cleveland Clinic. Susan and I opted not to return to Florida immediately. We stayed in the hotel located on the Cleveland Clinic campus for two more days for our peace of mind. Finally on Friday, November 17th, one week following my life-changing surgery, Susan and I boarded a flight in Cleveland for the return trip to Orlando and then on home to Ocala.

As our flight became airborne, I glanced out the window at the city below. Thoughts of my initial scouting trip to the Cleveland Clinic just two months earlier, came to mind. Then I came afflicted by a major disease. I came seeking help. I came harboring hope.

Now I found myself leaving town with a burden lifted. The first half of my surgical revitalization was complete. Now came a time of healing in preparation for stage two.

As the city of Cleveland and the Cleveland Clinic disappeared behind us, I took inventory of my recent experience. Behind I left my ulcerative colitis and the diseased colon that was inflamed by it. Behind I left the fear and anxious anticipation of major surgery. Behind I left a mask of false bravado and manufactured courage.

Infinitely more important than all those things, I left holding "the bag"—and clutching the newfound health and hope it represented.

11

My New Reality

The flight from Cleveland to Orlando was exhausting but otherwise uneventful. I intended to sleep. I've slept on hundreds of flights over the years. But this time sleep wouldn't come. There was too much to think about. So much had happened during the past week that I had trouble concentrating on just one thing. As my mind skipped from one perspective to another and then back again, I struggled to process it all.

I thought about the people around me during the trip.

I have flown hundreds of times over the past twenty years on business—more than one and a half million air miles in total. I have encountered hundreds of individuals on planes and in airports who had noticeable physical restrictions and limitations. I hate to admit it, but I basically ignored them. Not until today could I really relate to their plight.

I better understand their struggles now that I have shuffled from the hotel lobby to the taxi like some infirm old man, unable to carry even my own bag. At the airport I was dependent on a wheelchair and assistance to get from point A to point B.

At the security checkpoint, the staples in my stomach used to knit my incision together set off the metal detector. Before I could explain, an overzealous security agent began patting my stomach in search of hidden objects. I was sickened by the wave of pain that swept over me. But there was no time to delay. They wanted me to keep moving. I was holding up their line.

In the past I had noticed others who were struggling. What could I—should I—have done to help? Will I be more observant in the future? Will I be more empathetic of their needs? Will I offer my assistance? If I won't, who will? If I don't, what does that say about me as a person?

I thought about my recovery.

Immediately following the surgery I was as helpless as a newborn baby. Less than a week ago I could do virtually nothing for myself. I couldn't bathe, laugh, cough, sit up, roll over or do a thousand other things I otherwise took for granted without experiencing horrendous, piercing pain in my midsection.

I constantly needed help. I needed help getting in and out of bed. I needed help getting to the bathroom, bathing, dressing and eating.

My sleep was measured in minutes, not hours.

I lived on chicken broth and Jello.

Now, seven short days later, I can feel my body healing. I'm not where I want to be, but I'm so much better than I was. Although the pain is still present, it's more tolerable with each passing day.

With each stage of my improvement, I regain a bit more of my independence. Instead of calling for help, I get up when I need to relieve myself. I walked the length of the hotel corridor ten times this morning, unassisted. I was slow and deliberate, but in control.

I showered this morning without Susan's help. Shaving, washing my hair, bathing, toweling off—as tiring as it was, it invigorated me.

Breakfast today consisted of scrambled eggs, toast and juice. My appetite is returning.

Today marks the first time in a week that I have had any interest in what information a newspaper might provide me.

I guess it's true that progress is sometimes measured in inches, not miles. And the little things in life do matter.

I thought about my ileostomy—my bag.

I wonder if this gentleman sitting beside me knows I'm wearing a bag. Does he have any idea what I've been through? I know. Susan knows. But does this guy know? How could he? Even if he knew, would he care? Why should he? He doesn't know me. He doesn't care about me.

I have worried that the bag would be obvious to others. But it's really not. As I sit here looking down at my lap, it's not even noticeable to me. I was concerned about an offensive odor, but there has been none. Apparently the bags are designed and constructed to contain not only waste but the accompanying gas and odor as well.

It's really quiet, too. I rarely hear any sound coming from it. And when I do, it's no different or more noticeable than when someone's belly growls.

It's there. I know it is. But what about the rest of the world? They truly are oblivious.

I thought about my future.

I'm healing and the ileostomy is working well. For that I'm thankful. Now I must learn patience.

I'm grounded for at least the next two weeks. The doctors were adamant that I not drive. The risk of tearing something loose inside me is just too high. No big deal. I don't feel like driving anyway. I'll let Susan and my buddies chauffeur me around for a while.

They also told me that it will take four to six weeks before I'm strong enough to resume most of my normal, non-strenuous activities. That will be tougher. I need to get back to work. But I also recognize that I need the rest. I have been working since I was thirteen years old. Not once since then have I been idle for four straight weeks, much less six. This will be a new experience—a test. On the other hand, maybe I'll like it.

My first priority is to get strong and healthy for February 23rd. Ninety-eight days from today. That's when I'm scheduled to be back in Cleveland for the reversal surgery—the reconnection. They have assured me again and again that it is much easier to reconnect the plumbing than it is to create new plumbing in the first place. The second surgery has been described as a piece of cake compared to what I have just endured. Less intrusive. Easier to bounce back. I hope they are right.

Ninety-eight days. I've had clients take longer than that to pay their bill. I waited them out. I can wait this thing out, too.

I thought about my friends and family.

It was great to have the gang with me in Cleveland. Even better than I expected. I think all would agree that we shared a unique, unforgettable experience.

They were all a great encouragement to me. But I believe they may have helped Susan even more. They were good company for her. Their presence and conversation kept her mind and time occupied. Had they not come, I'm sure she would have stayed by my bedside non-stop—worrying. She didn't need that and neither did I.

Now another unique experience awaits. I can't wait to see Joe, Sarah and Sophie. But they have never seen me like this. They have no idea what to expect. When I spoke with them by phone from the hospital, they were more interested in sharing what I was missing in their lives. I was fine with that. That's the way it should be. How could I have described my situation to them in a way they would have visualized and understood anyway?

Now, though, I'm wondering what their reaction will be when they see me. My labored movement. My slightly drawn posture. What will they think? How will they react? Will they be frightened?

I'm sure they will be glad to see me. They always are whenever I've been away on an extended business trip. But how much will they want to know about the details of what I've just been through? For that matter, how much do I want to share with them? Will they be interested in seeing my incision and the staples? Joe probably will. Most thirteen-year-old boys are inexplicably drawn to a certain measure of gore. The girls? I really don't know. Maybe, maybe not. It may be a bit too graphic—too gruesome for their tastes.

Interested or not, either way is fine with me. I'm just glad to be going home.

We began our final approach into Orlando. Once back on the ground, we waited as the other passengers deplaned. We then made our way off the plane to my waiting chariot (a.k.a. a borrowed wheelchair). Susan wheeled me dutifully through the concourse to the baggage claim area. There we found two smiling faces awaiting our arrival.

Longtime friends, Charlie and Margaret Elder, welcomed us warmly. But their smiles couldn't hide their concern. My frail appearance and halting, deliberate, shuffling movements were obviously disconcerting to them.

Half an hour later we had collected our luggage and were motoring up the Florida Turnpike on our way back to Ocala. As we settled in for the eighty-five mile trip, Margaret presented me with a plastic container of homemade applesauce. It was sweet and delicious—the best I had ever eaten. After a week of institutional food, it tasted like nectar from the gods. I ate slowly, relishing every bite, careful not to get any on my face for fear my tongue would slap me to death trying to get at it.

Back home as we pulled into our driveway, the headlights illuminated a little face peering out from one of the bedroom windows. A sentry had been posted. It was Sophie. Her eyes were dancing and her smile beamed from ear-to-ear. As soon as she spotted us, the face disappeared from the window and seconds later reappeared in the driveway. With her were Joe, Sarah and my mother. The reunion was emotional and spontaneous. I became convinced that a driveway is the perfect place for a family's reunion. It was great to be home.

"Daddy, I love you and I'm glad you're home," Sophie gushed. "Did you bring me something?"

"We probably can find something for a good six-year-old girl. Have you been good?" I asked.

"I've been really good, haven't I, Bobba?" she asked, drawing my mother into the conversation for official verification.

Mom nodded and smiled as she stepped forward to greet Susan and me with a warm hug and kiss.

"Welcome home, Phil," she said. "The kids missed you and Susan. We all did. Let's go in the house. Supper is almost ready."

Sarah and Joe scurried around excitedly as they ferried our bags from the car to the house. We convinced the Elders to join us for supper and we all headed inside.

As the final meal preparations were being made, Joe pulled me aside and into his bedroom. He shut the door behind us.

"Joe, I missed you," I said.

"I missed you, too," he said impatiently. "Now let me see."

"Let you see what?"

"You know what! I want to see where they cut you open."

"Well, thanks, Joe, for your overwhelming compassion and concern, not to mention the delicate way you have handled this touching emotional moment," I teased sarcastically.

"I'm sorry, but you know what I mean," he protested. "They

told me it was a big cut. Is it?"

"Yeah, it's pretty big. And if you want to see it, I'll show you. But before I do, go ask your sisters if they are interested in seeing it, too. There will be only one showing tonight."

Joe hustled out of the room. Seconds later, from down the hall, I clearly heard Sarah say, "Oh, that's groooooooss!" Almost immediately I heard Sophie mimic her sister by repeating exactly the same words and attempting to replicate the exaggerated, disgusted tone of an eleven-year-old. Joe sprinted back down the hall and into the room, slamming the door behind him.

"They don't want to see it," he said breathlessly. "But I do. Show me."

"Okay, I will. But only on one condition. You've got to promise me that if you have any questions, you'll go ahead and ask them. I want to be sure you understand as much about this whole thing as possible. Is it a deal?"

"Sure."

I unbuttoned my shirt revealing the large gauze dressing loosely covering my wound. Slowly, I peeled the dressing back. As I did, Joe seemed at first mesmerized and then a bit taken aback by the full magnitude of what he was seeing. A slight involuntary grimace appeared on his face.

"Wow," he said with more shock than amazement. "That's a lot bigger than I expected."

"And that's not all of it. What you're seeing is about half the length of the total incision. To show you the rest of it I would have to drop my pants and underwear."

"No, that's okay," Joe said quickly. He continued to stare.

In a matter of seconds, the questions came.

How bad does it hurt? Why did they use staples instead of stitches? When will the staples come out? How will they get them out? Who will do it? How long will it take before you can throw a baseball with me again? Will the scar always be that big or will it eventually go away? How deep did they cut you? Are there a lot more stitches inside your belly? How many? When you go back for the next surgery, will they cut you in the same place?

The questions came in torrents, typical of a thirteen-year-old. I answered each one as simply and honestly as I could. Some were harder than others. A few were impossible for me to answer. Generally, though, my responses seemed to satisfy his unbounded curiosity. Then he hit me with the big one.

"Okay, I'm ready. Can I see the rest now?" he asked seriously.

"Joe, I told you the incision is just like what you're looking at now only further down."

"I don't mean that," he said impatiently. "I want to see your bag. I know you have one. Mom told us why you have to wear one. The girls don't want to see it, but I do."

"I see. Are you sure?" I asked.

"I'm sure."

"Okay, but the deal is the same."

Slowly I unbuckled my belt and then my pants. I slid the pants down a few inches below my waistline until the exposed intestine and the top of the bag were clearly visible. Joe looked on in wonderment. He bent down, his face mere inches from the appliance to get a closer look.

For the next several minutes, Joe and I engaged in a frank,

rather detailed question and answer session regarding proctocolectomies, temporary loop ileostomies, stomas, bowel activity and, of course, the appliance itself. His questions proved to be most of the same ones I had asked Dr. Truesdale, Dr. Lavery, the E.T. nurse and others during the past eighteen months. My candid answers were fashioned from information gleaned from discussions with healthcare professionals, exhaustive research, and, of course, personal experience.

The give-and-take session with Joe helped me realize there are very few truly original questions. The questions Joe asked me were the same ones I had asked others…and the same ones that tens of thousands of people around the world continue to ask daily. The quest for answers—and understanding—drives us all.

Life consists of the same questions being asked over and over, but by different people in different situations. The people asking these questions may be ignorant, curious, uninformed, scared or uneducated, but they all have some level of interest or personal need that drives them. Without sufficient answers to their questions—or sources to rely on—the unknowns these individuals are left to deal with can be emotionally terrifying and psychologically paralyzing. That is certainly true of those who suffer from ulcerative colitis and IBD, along with those who love and support them.

During our impromptu gastrointestinal lesson I was surprised at just how much practical information I had previously catalogued and was now able to convey. I was just as surprised at Joe's level of interest.

I discovered that sharing information and breaking down barriers is easier when both parties are honest and genuinely interested in the welfare of the other. Joe cared about my health and well being. I cared about Joe's understanding and peace of mind. As a result of our shared concern for each other, the communication and bond between us was enhanced.

The first few days back home were good ones. We enjoyed a steady stream of visitors, along with numerous get-well cards, calls and e-mails. The attention helped take my mind off my soreness and general level of discomfort.

Still, I tired easily; so I tried to rest as much as I could. I found it more comfortable to sleep in the recliner than our tall, four-poster bed. It was simply less taxing to get in and out.

One thing I took great pleasure in during the early days of my convalescence was eating. For the first time in almost two years, I could eat without the fear of cramping, fever, abdominal pain and diarrhea that had marked my extended battle with ulcerative colitis. That problem was alleviated when I surrendered my colon. Of course, while I wore the ostomy bag I continued to be careful about certain foods the E.T. nurse had identified as "no-nos."

For the first two weeks following my return from the hospital, folks from our church insisted on providing the evening meal for our family. Their thoughtfulness and generosity temporarily freed Susan from major meal preparation. So she was able to attend to other pressing responsibilities associated with our business, our home, our children, and, of course, her temporarily incapacitated husband. I always thought that if Susan ever decided to run off and join the circus, she would make a great juggler. She had been masterfully juggling a myriad of duties for years.

Therefore, when various individuals called to announce their intentions to deliver a meal, we were all appreciative. Before long we were also overwhelmed—and overfed. One night the menu might feature ham or chicken with all the fixings. The next night might have an Italian flair with a pasta dish, salad and garlic bread. Casseroles were very popular. Each night's fare was better than the night before.

I remember one meal in particular. It was lovingly prepared by Vanja Johnson, a native Northeasterner who had retired to Florida with her husband, Art. The couple arrived on our doorstep bearing Vanja's specialty—Yankee pot roast accompanied by ample helpings of potatoes, carrots and beans and fresh bread. For dessert she had prepared a wonderful homemade apple pie.

I was in heaven. I ate like I hadn't eaten in days. In actuality, I hadn't eaten like that in months. My ulcerative colitis would never have allowed it. But no longer. I gorged myself. When I finally waddled away from the table, I looked like a pot-gutted puppy. I was so full my shrunken belly was literally stretched tight. I could actually feel a tugging sensation at the staples which bound me together.

With supper over and my plate clean, I made my way to the couch where I reclined and reached for the television remote. Soon, I was joined in the room by Susan and Joe. Together we settled into a blessed evening of familial inactivity.

After a short time in the relative quiet of our living room, my belly gradually began to actively rumble and gurgle. I knew what was happening. Deep in my stomach the acids and digestive juices were working to break down my recently completed feast. As a byproduct of this process, natural intestinal gases were forming. With my digestive pipes having recently been reconstructed and detoured, there was only one place for the forming gases to go.

Pfuuutt.

The involuntary emission pierced the solitude of the room. Joe's head jerked up as he turned to face me. "What was that?" he asked.

Slightly embarrassed, I responded, "It was my bag. I ate too much supper. Something obviously has given me gas."

"That was your bag? It can do that?" Joe asked with adolescent excitement. "I never thought about what happens to you now if you have gas," he added almost wistfully.

Susan sat resolutely focused on the TV screen. She refused to acknowledge the give-and-take between Joe and me.

Suddenly—pfffuuuuttt. The sound of another emission. This time a little longer and louder than before. Like a flash, Joe bounded out of his chair and slid across the floor on his knees coming to a stop beside me and the couch.

"It did it again, didn't it?" he asked excitedly.

"Yeah, I can't help it. My belly is as tight as it can be," I chuckled, beginning to get caught up in Joe's youthful enthusiasm.

Susan continued to pretend that Joe and I were temporarily not on this planet.

"Can I feel your stomach?" Joe asked.

"Sure. But be gentle. I'm still very sore."

Joe laid his hand on my stomach and applied a gentle little push. As he did, the pressure forced a new burst of gaseous air from my bloated stomach, through my small intestine, out the stoma and into the rapidly inflating bag. The sound repeated itself.

Pffuuuttt!

Joe literally collapsed on the floor rolling in gales of laughter. Eventually he would compose himself slightly and return to press again and again. The result was always the same.

Pffuut. Pffuuut. Pffuutt.

To Joe the whole experience was hilarious. His youthful antics and unbridled laughter were contagious. Soon I was laughing just as hard—with him and at him. Even Susan gave in. She could hold back no longer. For several minutes the three of us just sat and hee-hawed together at a situation over which I had no control—a situation that some might view as anything but laughable.

From that point on we all seemed to relax a bit. My current physical condition, though still of critical importance to us all, somehow became a little less serious—a little easier to laugh about.

A few weeks later, in early December, just prior to the Christmas holidays, Susan and I were invited guests at parties on back-to-back evenings. I was not even close to being completely healed but I felt good enough to be with people again. More months than I cared to think about had passed since I had been able to attend a dinner party without worrying that the lion's share of my time would be spent closeted away in the host's bathroom.

Unfortunately, during these two evenings, I allowed the excitement of the good times to outweigh sound judgement.

During the first party I deliberately ignored my E.T.'s earlier advice to avoid any meat that I could not cut with a fork. She had specifically warned that tough stringy meat was especially hard to digest and could create a painful and potentially dangerous obstruction at the point of my newly created stoma. Nevertheless, when the evening's entrée, a lovely center cut pork chop, was served, I climbed into the feeding trough with both feet. The meal was delicious. I cleaned my plate. But the price I was to pay for my temporary indulgence was steep.

That night, until well past sunrise the next morning, I was miserable. As my meal worked its way through my digestive system, the harder-to-digest portions of pork hindered and backed up the flow of waste discharge. Until the meat had softened and broken down sufficiently to pass though the stoma's restricted opening, the pressure and pain caused by the accumulating waste behind the temporary obstruction continued to build. The effect and related discomfort were similar in concept to a baby making its way through a restricted birth canal—or a camel through the eye of a needle!

Unable to sleep through this excruciating, seemingly endless process, I paced the floor, desperate for relief from my self-inflicted pain. After ten hours or so, the waste thankfully made its way through my system and into the waiting appliance.

I was thankful, but apparently not much wiser, because no more than twenty-four hours following this initial episode, we found ourselves at Party Number Two. And despite Susan's cautionary warnings of "remember last night," I cheerfully accepted the ribeye steak when it was offered. I reasoned with myself that smaller bites and more thorough chewing would yield a significantly different result than the night before. I was wrong again.

The outcome was worse. Though I didn't think it possible, the second night was even more miserable than the first. By the time the sun rose on the second morning, I had retired my knife and had finally learned my lesson:

DON'T BE A DORK—USE JUST A FORK!

Though I had learned a difficult but valuable lesson, I still hungered for a little sympathy. I certainly wasn't getting it at home. Despite my most pitiful moaning and groaning, all I got from Susan was her telltale "didn't I tell you so?" look. So when my brother-in-law, Sam Dunning, called at midday following my second sleepless night, I saw an opportunity to invite company to my misery.

"Phil, I'm sorry I haven't talked to you in a while," Sam began apologetically. "I'm just calling to see how you are feeling."

This is great, I thought. *He already feels bad for not calling. This is just the opportunity I have been longing for. Sam will understand what I have been through. Good Old Sam will be happy to feel sorry for me.*

"Sam, thanks for calling," I said before shifting into my personal 'pity party' mode. "I've been feeling pretty good recently. But honestly, the last two nights have been two of my worst yet."

Susan could hear my self-serving comments from the kitchen. I watched as she just rolled her eyes heavenward. On the other hand, Sam seemed genuinely concerned.

"Phil, what's the problem? Have you had a setback? Is it an infection of some sort? Have you seen the doctor?"

"No, Sam, it's nothing like that. I'm fine now. It's just that I was told not to eat meat too tough to be cut with a fork, but for the past two nights I did. As a result I have had two really rough nights."

I paused instinctively, allowing Sam the opportunity to insert some sort of compassionate reassurance. I expected a response. And respond he did.

"Well, then," he said flatly, "I guess you might as well be walking around with a flashing neon sign over your head that reads: DUMB ASS! DUMB ASS! DUMB ASS!"

Sam's response caught me completely by surprise. I was initially stunned. But on the other hand, what else was there to say? The truth was the truth. We exploded into spontaneous laughter.

Sam's irreverent comeback wasn't what I had expected. But he was absolutely right. If information is readily available and clearly communicated and one chooses to callously ignore that information, there is very little question in the minds of onlookers as to what that person is—and what I was.

As these and other harmless experiences unfolded, I began to realize that as important as it was for my body to heal, it was equally important that my mind and spirit heal as well.

There is no question that my condition was serious. My surgery was serious. Now my recuperation in preparation for the reconnecting surgery is serious, too. But none of this provides justification for taking myself too seriously. I need to lighten up. It can always be a lot worse than what I am experiencing now.

Thankfully, I evolved to the point that I could laugh easily at myself and my new reality. As a result, a delightfully solid foundation on which I could build my post-operative future was laid. I pulled the plug on the neon sign. No need to be a "dumb ass" forever.

12

The Next Big Thing

Many experiences and lessons knit themselves together to form the fabric of the one hundred five days between my initial surgery and the scheduled reconnection. It was a difficult and challenging time—physically, emotionally and psychologically. It was also a period of adjustment, adaptation and reassessment for both mind and body.

I distinctly remember good days—days full of promise and hope. But other days—fewer in number—challenged my optimism and resolve. I remember times when I laughed long and loud and other times when my tears freely flowed. I spent expectant days planning my recovery and sleepless nights dreading a relapse. I could see both good and bad in the overall experience. This period of recuperation was, in fact, a microcosm of real life—my life.

Though my doctors assured me I was convalescing nicely, there was still much uncertainty with which I had to deal.

Oh, man, I'm sore! I never imagined a body could be this sore. How much longer will it last? It takes forever for me to do the simplest things like getting up from the table or climbing in and out of a car. I don't know why they went to the trouble of telling me that I shouldn't be lifting anything that weighed more than five pounds. I can barely lift a full glass of iced tea, for heaven's sake. If I were to sneeze, I think I would just die right on the spot.

On top of all that, I need to get back to work. How long can the company continue without me? The speaking business is too often an "out of sight, out of mind" business. My clients need to know I am available. Susan and Kim need to see me in harness—working at my desk. They need to be reassured that I'm at least trying to get back in the saddle, that I'm trying to pull my weight. But I can't work. I can't even concentrate right now.

When will my stamina return? Watching television, reading, talking with visitors, all are exhausting. I want to get stronger. To get better, I've got to get stronger. But when will I? And how?

With so much uncertainty surrounding me, I began to search diligently for anchors—unshakable truths to cling to. I was desperate to find something I could believe in and count on. I was convinced I needed an activity that would make me feel as if I were doing something—anything—to help improve my current situation and myself.

I began to consciously recount all that I knew to be true as it related to my new situation. For example, I was learning that specific foods would elicit a predictable (favorable or unfavorable) reaction—just as I had been told. I became well aware that extended periods of rest were critical—just as I had been told. And I had discovered the therapeutic value of walking—just as I had been told.

While I was at the Cleveland Clinic, nurses and doctors alike had made a point of stressing to me the importance of walking. They emphasized again and again that the more I walked, the better I would feel and the quicker I would heal. While there, I had discovered they were right.

In the hours and days immediately following my surgery, I struggled to walk even the length of the corridor outside my hospital room. The pain was great and my stamina was severely limited. But with the encouragement of hospital staff and my family and friends, I stayed at it. Soon I began to notice that instead of each lap becoming more difficult and laborious, strangely enough each lap seemed a bit easier than the one before. I could actually feel myself growing stronger, evidenced by my ability to walk farther and faster with each outing.

Once I was back home, my first few pedestrian outings were fairly feeble. No longer surrounded by the friendly confines of a hospital ward with professional attendants standing by, I now had to continue my progress in an environment of my own making.

I began by walking to the mailbox—less than forty yards roundtrip—two or three times a day. Soon I had progressed to a couple hundred yards per outing. Each effort felt better than the one before. Emboldened by my progress, I promised myself I would walk every day. I began to keep a daily log.

On November 20th, ten days following surgery, I walked a grand total of one half mile. It took over twenty minutes. It was discouraging, but I didn't give up. For the next two weeks I shuffled on gamely.

On December 4th I walked a complete mile in twenty-three minutes. Motivated by having finally broken the one mile mark, the next day I pushed myself and walked two miles in forty-seven minutes. I continued pounding the pavement. With each passing day my time and distance improved.

December 19th found me walking *three* miles in forty-seven minutes. Three days later I walked four full miles in seventy-one minutes. I rang in the new year by walking five miles in less than eighty-five minutes. By mid-February I was back on the track jogging.

My pain and soreness gradually subsided as my strength and stamina returned. One by one, the one hundred five days ticked away as my body healed and my confidence grew.

I also began working again. At first I was only able to spend a quiet hour or so at my desk catching up on reading and paperwork. As the days passed, I worked longer until finally, on January 8th, just twenty-eight days following surgery, I traveled to Richmond, Virginia, for my first post-surgical speaking engagement. It was a tough one. I led a six-hour leadership seminar for managers from country clubs all over Virginia. By the time the day was over, I was totally exhausted—and totally exhilarated!

I did it! I'm back. Back to work. Back doing what I love to do. My audience members were totally unaware that I had ever been sick.

They were clueless that this was my first program back following major surgery. They had no idea I was wearing a bag.

I can still do this! I just proved I can. I just did it!

With my confidence buoyed by the success of that first program, I turned my attention to the upcoming surgical procedure designed to entirely eliminate the need for my loop ileostomy.

From that pivotal moment of decision the previous August when I opted to go through with the proctocolectomy and J-pouch anastomosis procedures, I actually began to look forward to the *second* surgery.

I never kidded myself. I knew surgery number one would be difficult for me for a number of reasons—difficult because I had never experienced major surgery before. Difficult because I knew the recuperation period would be long and arduous. Difficult because I would be unable to work for an extended period. And, of course, difficult because of the mental and physical adjustments that wearing a bag would necessitate. No, sir, surgery number one was not something I had looked forward to.

On the other hand, from the very beginning I had viewed surgery number two in a totally different light. My reasoning was practical. Everything I had read or heard about surgery number two—the reconnection—indicated it was fairly minor in comparison to the initial procedure. It would be less intrusive. No removal of a major organ this time. No need for the extensive construction of a replacement waste storage and removal system.

Simply put, the surgeons would eliminate the need for the bag by closing the loop ileostomy. To do so, a basic incision would be made through the abdominal wall around the ileostomy. Then the stoma would be closed by sewing the two ends of the exposed ileum back together before repositioning the intestine in the abdominal cavity. Finally, the opening in the abdominal wall, where the stoma had been positioned, would be closed using the appropriate ***suture*** material.

After that, there was nothing more to do but wait for nature to work its recuperative wonders.

As time quickly approached for surgery number two, I felt I was ready—physically, mentally and emotionally—I was ready.

In the final days leading up to my return to the Cleveland Clinic, I made major speeches for two well-known corporate clients. I spoke at the international gathering of Kentucky Fried Chicken (KFC) franchise owners at their annual convention in Las Vegas. A few days later I traveled to Princeton, New Jersey, to address a group of managers for Verizon Wireless Connected Solutions. For both programs I was well prepared and confident. As a result, both programs went off without a hitch.

That was exactly how I felt as I rolled back into Cleveland—well prepared and confident. My focus was clear. I was certain this procedure would go off without a hitch as well.

Now all I have to do is get this second little surgery behind me and then get on with my life.

I saw a number of similarities between this return trip and the one that preceded it by three and a half months. I was headed back to the same hospital. My former surgeon, Dr. Ian Lavery, would once again be leading the surgical team. And, as before, I was accompanied by my core supporters—Susan, my siblings and this time, my mother and her husband. On this occasion Susan's parents volunteered to travel to Florida to be with our children.

Because of the similarities—"the knowns"—of what I had already been through, as well as the confidence that the worst part of my surgical saga was past, I arrived in Cleveland in a remarkably upbeat state of mind.

It's hard to believe the time is already here. The experience has been tough—but not as tough as it might have been. I expected these past one hundred five days to seem like an eternity. But that hasn't been the case at all.

Maybe it hasn't seemed so long because I haven't hated my ileostomy. I expected to. I really did. From the very beginning I wondered within myself how I would ever be able to adjust and adapt to wearing one. It all seemed so...unnatural.

But that was then. This is now. Now I know what wearing one is really like. I don't have to imagine how it might be based on someone else's description. Now I've been there...done that. Instead of a T-shirt, I have a pretty ghoulish scar to prove it.

The bag was inconvenient. No question about it. And I was self-conscious about wearing it, at least in the beginning. But now, I know the truth.

Because of the first surgery—including the ileostomy—I feel better now than I have felt in three years! In reality, the bag has done little to impede my life activities. In fact, I can't think of one thing I could do before the surgery that I couldn't do now if I really wanted to.

On top of that, my appetite is back. I am exercising again at virtually the same level of intensity that I was before the surgery. I'm still wearing my old clothes—the ones that some ill-informed individuals warned me I would have to cast off because of the bag. I haven't purchased even one new item of clothing to accommodate it. There has been no need.

My overall surgical and recovery experience had been so generally positive that I spent almost no time considering what might go wrong with the second surgery. Instead, I spent almost all my time thinking about the immediate future. And the future was looking very bright.

My business phone was ringing. People were requesting my speaking and training services. I had been on the sidelines, but now I was back in the game. I had no desire to return to the sidelines. At least, not for any significant amount of time. So when presented with the opportunity to book a speaking engagement on March 11th—sixteen short days after the second scheduled surgery—I jumped at the opportunity.

The doctors informed me that the average person isn't ready to return to work after the first surgery for eight weeks or longer. I was back at work—on stage—in just twenty-eight days. Therefore, I must not be average. Sure, I was tired and worn out after it was over—but I did it. And that was after a BIG surgery. This next surgery is just a reconnection.

Everything I've read or heard says that the reconnection is much easier to bounce back from. They say the average person should expect to be off work for four to six weeks. Well, that's easy for them to say. They must not have a business to run and a payroll to meet. If it takes the average person thirty to forty-five days, I should be ready in sixteen!

My thinking was bolstered by my rapidly improving health. I had already begun the process of forgetting those long sleepless nights of post-operative pain and discomfort that were so real to me just a few weeks earlier. I returned to the campus of the Cleveland Clinic on a mission.

I'm going to get this behind me as quickly as possible and get on with my life.

The pre-surgical procedure mirrored the previous one almost exactly. There was paperwork to be completed and blood to be drawn. The E.T. on duty reassured me that my stoma had healed perfectly and was in fine condition to be tucked back into my abdomen. Finally, after more than three hours of regimentation, moving from station to station and task to task, I found myself back in the same examination room waiting for the doctor whom I had first met during my initial scouting trip six months earlier.

I think it's amazing how things that only take a few moments of time to occur can change a person's perspective—and life—forever.

I had been foolishly battling diarrhea alone for months, but it wasn't until the moment I spotted blood in the toilet that I got serious about seeing a doctor.

It took but a few short moments during my first colonoscopy for Dr. Truesdale to diagnose and communicate my ulcerative colitis.

A few moments alone in a Washington, D.C., hotel room led me to finally decide to surrender my colon to medical science.

Just moments with a new doctor during an office visit and I decided he was the one to do life changing surgery on me.

And now, in just a few moments, we will meet again to discuss my life without an ileostomy.

I was lost in silent thought as Dr. Lavery entered the room. This time he was trailed by only one white-coated doctor-in-training.

"Hello, Phil," he said as we shook hands. I offered my hand to the student-doctor but decided against initiating any in-depth conversation.

"Hi, doctor. How are you?"

"I'm fine, thank you. But the question is, how are you? Are you ready for tomorrow?"

"I've been doing well and I'm more than ready," I admitted honestly.

"Good. I see no reason why the surgery can't proceed as scheduled."

Dr. Lavery and I continued our casual conversation as he attended to those items on the pre-surgical checklist. The appointment moved quickly.

"Phil, I'm sure you are ready for the reconnection, but I'm curious. How has it been with the loop ileostomy?"

"I'm glad you asked," I admitted. "I've been thinking a lot about that very thing recently. You're right. I am ready for the reconnection. But I must admit, I have arrived at a strange place in my thinking."

"Really? What is it?"

"Well, doc, the difference between the way I feel now and the way I felt when we first met is the equivalent difference to daylight and dark. Recovering from the surgery was challenging, but otherwise I feel great—so good, in fact, I want you to know that if for some reason something goes wrong in surgery tomorrow and the reconnection is not possible, I will still say I made a good decision by coming here. I would gladly live the rest of my life with a bag instead of a colon if it meant I could feel as good as I do now."

As I finished my statement, my voice began to choke with emotion. Dr. Lavery listened intently and smiled.

"I'm certainly glad you feel that way," he countered, "but I see absolutely no indications of any problems. By this time tomorrow you should be on your way to recuperating completely. Do you have any last minute questions for me?"

"None that I can think of," I said.

"Good. Then I will catch up with you in surgery tomorrow morning. Enjoy your evening."

I left Dr. Lavery's office with one thought.

Soon this will all be over.

That evening I retired and slept soundly. The next morning Susan and I were up early and at the surgical building before our scheduled time. Nevertheless, they were ready for me. I was quickly whisked away to PreCare and readied for surgery. Unlike the previous occasion, there were no delays this time.

"Mrs. Van Hooser, it looks like I am going to have to steal your husband away from you. They are ready for him in surgery," were the words of the PreCare attendant. "They just called and asked us to bring him up."

Susan turned her attention to me as a lay on the gurney. My IV had already been started.

"So, Phil, are you ready?" she asked.

"You betcha," I said. And I meant it. "I'll see all of you in a little while. Go get some breakfast. We've about got this thing whipped."

Susan gave me a quick kiss as they wheeled me away. This time there were no delays. No stopovers in the surgical staging area. No war movie reruns to watch on television. Instead, I was delivered directly to a nurse who stood waiting in the hallway just outside an operating room.

"Good morning," was the pleasant greeting that came from behind the surgical mask.

"Good morning," I replied comfortably.

"Sir, would you please tell me your name?" she asked while referring to the paperwork she was holding.

"My name is Phillip Van Hooser and I am scheduled to have Dr. Lavery reverse and reconnect a temporary loop ileostomy," I answered before allowing her the opportunity to ask her next predictable question.

Her eyes sparkled as she looked up at me over the blue mask.

"So, you know the drill, huh?" she asked good-naturedly.

"Yep, I'm a surgical veteran," I said with a chuckle.

"Well, we're ready for you. Let's roll you in and get you started."

"Sounds good to me."

As we entered the O.R., I noticed three or four other masked nurses busily engaged in their respective activities. My gurney was rolled along side the operating table positioned in the middle of the room. With minimal assistance from the nurses, I lifted and scooted myself off the gurney and onto the table. I remember the chilling sensation as my bare bottom—uncovered by my hospital gown—brushed against the cold bare metal of the table.

"Oooh, that's invigorating," I said with a chuckle to no one in particular.

Once I was appropriately situated, one of the attendants started fiddling with my IV line.

"Mr. Van Hooser, I am starting your anesthesia now. You will be getting sleepy soon."

"Okay. I'm ready for a good nap."

"I see you are here to have your loop ileostomy closed. You shouldn't be with us very long at all. And you've already been through the hardest part. Compared to your first surgery, this one will be a piece of cake."

"That's what I'm counting on," I said as I began to feel my eyelids getting heavy. I just lay back and relaxed.

The last conscious recollection I had before drifting completely away was the words of that nurse. I replayed them over and over in my head.

"…you've been through the hardest part…this one will be a piece of cake…a piece of cake…a…piece…of …"

I had no way of knowing how long I had been asleep. It could have been one hour or twenty-four for all I knew. But I clearly remember the first thought that came to me as I regained conscious awareness in the recovery room.

This doesn't feel like a piece of cake to me. This feels familiar. Much too familiar. I feel exactly like I felt after the first surgery.

The thought bothered me. I began to try to calm myself by looking for a logical explanation.

Relax. Don't worry. I'll bet this is just some psychological trick my subconscious is playing on me. I've probably thought so much about pain in recent months that my brain is creating the illusion of pain.

Or maybe I am experiencing a type of temporary flashback syndrome. The kind that happens to some people after they've dealt with some sort of traumatic experience. Maybe the sights, sounds and smells of this room are triggering a pain flashback. Maybe it will pass.

Then again, this may be just an old garden variety dream—or nightmare. Maybe I'm not really awake. Maybe I'm dreaming I'm awake. Maybe I'm not really hurting. Maybe I'm just dreaming I'm hurting.

I continued to lie still on the table. Trying to think. Trying to concentrate. Trying not to move. I blinked my eyes tightly over and over again in a futile attempt to flush away the anesthesia-induced cobwebs that lingered in my brain.

I may not have been completely awake, but I knew something was wrong. I was hurting. Eventually, I became uncomfortable enough that I decided to try to reposition myself. Slowly and deliberately I shifted my body position ever so slightly. But the movement caused a piercing pain to knife through my midsection.

"Owwwo."

My whispered guttural response was involuntary. But it yielded results. Almost immediately a nurse appeared and laid her hand on my shoulder.

"Mr. Van Hooser," she whispered softly. "Are you awake?"

"Yeah," I mumbled with my eyes still tightly closed. I could feel the grimace that made up my facial expression.

"Sir, how do you feel?" she asked quietly.

My response this time was not involuntary. This time there was no false bravado—no smokescreen. It was deliberate and delivered with real emotion.

"I hurt! (pause) I thought this surgery was supposed to be a piece of cake."

"Mr. Van Hooser, I'm sorry to tell you that they experienced some sort of unexpected difficulty during your surgery. Please let me reassure you—you are fine. The surgery was a complete success. It's just that it ended up being more extensive than they had planned."

That was exactly what I didn't want to hear.

Don't tell me more. I don't want to hear more right now.

About that time the nurse was called away for several minutes to attend to the needs of another patient. I was glad she left. It gave me time to think.

The surgery was a success. The surgery was a success. Phil, you've got to focus on the bright side. She said the surgery was a success.

(Pause)

Yeah, but man, it hurts!

Not again. I don't want to go through all this again.

As I lay there trying to make sense of my current state, emotion overtook me. But it wasn't emotion in general. This emotion was very specific. I got angry. I wasn't angry at anyone or anything in particular. I was just angry in general. Somehow my anger began to yield some measure of resolve and determination.

After a few minutes the nurse reappeared.

"Mr. Van Hooser, I don't know if you feel up to it or not, but you have some visitors waiting to see you whenever you're ready."

"I'm ready now," I said through gritted teeth.

The nurse stepped away from my bed and disappeared behind a curtain. Seconds later I saw two familiar faces. They were Susan and my sister Ellen. Both approached, each on an opposite side of my bed, carefully navigating their way past tubes, cords and expensive machinery. Susan took my hand. Ellen leaned over my bed and spoke first.

"So, Phil, how are you doing?" she asked as cheerfully as the situation would allow.

"I'm pissed!"

My direct and unpolished response seemed to catch both Ellen and Susan off guard. My words were neither previously planned nor carefully considered. There was no prior intent for them to be negative or mean-spirited. They were what they were—honest. It was an honest, gut level response that communicated my true feelings regarding a frustrating situation in which I found myself, but one over which I had very little control.

I turned my eyes toward Susan.

"What happened?" I asked directly.

Susan knew exactly what I was asking. There was no need to beat around the bush. There was no need to stall for a more appropriate time. She appeared to be prepared for the question.

"Phil, they did what they needed to do. Dr. Lavery called me during the surgery and informed me that they had discovered some ***adhesions***, or scar tissue, that had formed since the first surgery. Apparently, it is a common occurrence. But once the adhesions were discovered, they had to go in deeper to make sure they got them all. They did what they had to do. The surgery was a complete success."

Susan's explanation made perfect sense. Of course they needed to remove the adhesions before they became problematic and required future surgical attention. But I hadn't expected this. I hadn't planned for this. I was expecting a piece of cake.

Soon I was moved from the recovery room to a regular room. There I was surrounded once again by all of my family members. For the rest of the afternoon and into the evening, each did his or her best to be a source of encouragement. My pain had eased significantly due to Mark seizing immediate control of the PCA Pump. As a result, I was thinking more clearly and definitively. I began to formulate a new plan.

Around 9:00 p.m. the entire group said their "good nights" for the evening and began drifting away. As I expected, Susan was the last to leave.

"Phil, I know it's been a tough day for you. But you're doing great. Just get some rest. Tomorrow will be better."

She said "good-bye" and left.

Just after the group had departed, the night shift nurse entered my room. We chatted as she dutifully checked my blood pressure, pulse rate, medication levels and all the requisite monitors.

"Everything looks really good, Mr. Van Hooser. You're making my job easy. How do you feel?"

"I'm tired, but otherwise I suppose I'm doing okay."

"You have every reason to be tired. It's been a big day. Just get some rest. All there is to do now is to wait for the 'next big thing.'"

She grabbed my attention with the way she emphasized the phrase. I didn't understand what she meant. I had to know more.

"The 'next big thing?' What exactly are you talking about?"

"That's easy," she replied with a quick smile. "After a loop ileostomy closure like yours, the best indication that everything is working exactly as it should is that the patient passes gas. When gas makes its way through your system, that's our signal to start you on a liquid diet and shortly after that a soft diet. The sooner all that happens, the sooner you get to go home. That's a pretty big thing, don't you agree?"

"Absolutely. It's a real big thing to me," I said. "How long does it normally take?"

"Everybody is different. But usually 'the next big thing' happens, within twenty-four hours or so following surgery. Of course, when it happens we will want to know immediately. It's a big deal to us. So don't hesitate to call me, okay?"

Passing gas—the "next big thing" indeed. Her exuberance and playfulness reminded me of my son Joe's reaction when he first heard my bag filling with escaping gas. His reaction—and now hers—made me smile.

"You can count on me," I promised. "You will be the first to know."

The nurse left the room and flipped off the lights. I drifted off to sleep in search of much needed rest.

About 11:00 p.m. I awoke to a strange sensation. It was a sensation with which we are all familiar, but one I hadn't felt in several weeks. Down deep in my pelvic region I felt some mild pressure and I heard a low muted, rumbling sound.

I have since learned the scientific term for this occurrence is *borborygmus*: *intestinal rumbling caused by moving gas*. But at the time I immediately recognized it for what it really was—the "next big thing!"

Within minutes, the moment heralding the arrival of the "next big thing" occurred. I was elated. It was official. According to the nurse, my recovery was now officially in full swing. I reached for the "assistance call button." I had a promise to keep.

The nurse quickly appeared. "Yes, Mr. Van Hooser, you rang?"

"It happened," I said simply.

The nurse looked understandably confused.

"What happened, sir?"

"The 'next big thing,' of course. It just happened. You made me promise to let you know."

The nurse went from confused to almost giddy. Or at least as giddy as a professional caregiver will allow herself to become.

"Already? Why that's wonderful. Now it's just a matter of doing what we need to do to get you ready to go home. I'll make a note in your file. We will get you started on clear liquids first thing in the morning. Is there anything else you need now?"

"Yeah, there is one thing. When do you plan to get me up and walking? I haven't been out of this bed all day."

"Well, we really didn't intend to get you up until sometime tomorrow. It has been such a tough day for you we thought you would want to rest."

"You were right. I do want to rest. But I need to walk! Let me explain something. I have a very important speaking engagement for more than seven hundred people scheduled in just fifteen and a half days from now. I have had an unexpected setback today. But that doesn't change the fact that I plan to make that speech. I need to get up right now and start walking to get myself in shape for that presentation."

"You want to get up now? Are you sure?"

"That's right. I need to get up now," I replied. "Are you going to help me?" I asked as I slowly began to shift my body weight in an attempt to get my legs off the bed and over the side.

Recognizing my determination, the nurse stepped forward and offered her assistance. For the next ten minutes or so she accompanied me and my rolling IV stand as I made one complete loop around the hospital wing at nothing more than a snail's pace. By the time we returned to my room, I was exhausted. I leaned against the wall for support as the nurse rearranged my bedding.

While at the wall, I noticed a mounted grease board beside me. The nursing staff used it to leave written notes concerning patient care from one shift to the next. I retrieved a pen that was there, removed its cap and wrote simply "LAPS" followed by a single mark.

The nurse saw it and asked, "What's that for?"

"This board is going to keep me focused. I know how important walking is. I remember from the last time. I'm going to keep walking laps and keep making marks until I get out of here. Don't erase this, okay?"

"Okay," she said as she chuckled and shook her head slightly.

For the balance of that night, every time I was awakened for a temperature check or to take medication, I had the nurse get me up and take me for a walk. Upon our return, I would make my marks. The next day when my family returned to visit, I would have each one individually accompany me as I made my rounds. Again, we would log in the results.

On the third day of my hospital stay, I had progressed so rapidly that I was discharged from the hospital. As I gathered my belongings and sat waiting for the attendant to accompany me to the front of the hospital, I checked the grease board one final time. There they were—one hundred twenty-one marks! I had walked one hundred twenty-one laps around that hospital wing over a period of just three days—an average of approximately forty laps per day walked at intermittent times around the clock.

During my lifetime I have been privileged to hear the roar of the crowd as I scored a touchdown on an eighty-one yard pass play in a high school football game. I have been engulfed by teammates after hitting a homerun in a crucial baseball game. I have watched as hundreds of people rose in unison to bless me with a standing ovation following one of my speeches. Still, none of those experiences afforded me the indescribable feeling of accomplishment and satisfaction represented by those one hundred twenty-one hash marks and the realization of what it took to put them there.

Sixteen days after my reconnection surgery—adhesion removal not withstanding—I walked onto the stage at the Opryland Hotel and

Convention Center in Nashville, Tennessee. Before me sat more than seven hundred managers for Tractor Supply Company. For the next ninety minutes I spoke with power and conviction about the importance of personal motivation, frank communication, commitment, discipline, sacrifice and overall team support—each a vital element of leadership responsibility and success.

This was not a new message for me. It was one that I had shared with more than two thousand audiences and hundreds of thousands of individuals during the past dozen years. At the immediate conclusion of my remarks, seven hundred professional leaders responded with a thunderous standing ovation. Unaware of my recent health and medical challenges, their spontaneous response to my leadership message made their applause even more thrilling for me. It felt like old times again.

But it was not old times. This time something was different. I knew it. I could feel it. The difference was not so radical and blatant that the understanding of it was instantaneously obvious. No, it took awhile for me to recognize the specific difference. But eventually it sank in.

The difference was me. I was different. In the days and months that followed, I came to understand more clearly the significance of that difference.

In a period of about two years, I had fought an extended battle to save my colon and thereby restore my physical health. Before that battle began—before I was diagnosed with ulcerative colitis—my energies were expended on ordinary everyday activities—necessary activities, such as raising a family, making a living, securing a future, building a life. However, I labored on under the unspoken assumption that if I continued to do the ordinary things, eventually extraordinary results would occur.

But then I came face-to-face with IBD and the realities of living with a chronic illness. I didn't enlist. I was an unwilling soldier. I delayed joining the battle until it was obvious that it was my own blood that was being spilled; but once the battle was joined, I gave it my all.

The ordinary everyday activities of life were still important, but they were often overshadowed by the need to rally again and again against the flare-ups that attacked my physical, emotional, spiritual and psychological well being. This enemy was unlike any I had ever encountered. It was faceless. It was merciless. It resided deep in the inner linings of my gut. But the true battle was for my mind, heart and spirit.

Initially, I thought I could fight—and win—the battle alone. I believed that victory would come from being strong, independent and courageous. I believed that with minimal assistance from others, victory would be mine. I believed it, but I was wrong. In the end, I came to realize that I needed every bit of advice and direction I received from my medical caregivers and I needed every bit of love and support I received from my family and friends.

The battle was fierce. In the end my colon was lost. The ironic twist, however, came in recognizing what was gained by way of the loss.

During that two-year struggle, I gained a new appreciation for what it meant to suffer. As a result, I became more aware of the sufferings of others. Through struggle, I gained a new appreciation of support. As a result, I now look for positive ways to support others. Through struggle, I gained a new appreciation of generosity. As a result, I am now more ready to give without expectation of receiving anything in return.

These revelations have yielded extraordinary insights and opportunities for growth. During the battle, I eventually came to the realization that I could fight in isolation—but I could never win. To win I needed allies. In the end, I survived my ordeal because I allowed people who cared to join the battle. They strengthened me.

Now I have a debt to pay. There are millions of people around the world who suffer in various forms of pain and uncertainty. I must do what I can do. I must offer assistance, encouragement and support in whatever way I am able. I have been the beneficiary of such efforts from others. Therefore, it now becomes my obligation. Why? Because I strive to be a compassionate leader.

And that takes more than guts.

Conclusion

Seventeen months had passed since I surrendered my colon in the pursuit of restored health and vitality. Things were going well. My life was rebounding nicely. No complications. No setbacks. I felt great. Life was good.

Yet, as a professional speaker, I was finding it difficult to speak publicly about my personal struggle with IBD, ulcerative colitis and the surgeries. My emotions were just too close to the surface. So I took the easy way out. I simply kept the experience to myself. I treated it as "my little secret." That is, until I rolled into Scottsdale, Arizona.

I had been invited to address a group of public managers from around the United States. I was hired as their keynote conference speaker. Upon mounting the stage that day, I could sense an immediate connection with the audience. They were bright, energetic, warm, supportive and interested in my leadership perspective. I felt totally at ease with them.

As my presentation unfolded, although I hadn't planned to do so, for some reason I found myself sharing a brief portion of my "IBD story" to illustrate a concept from my leadership message. The lesson was an important one. It was one of those personal lessons from life that we all have—only I was sharing my lesson with these two hundred strangers whom I was suddenly treating as if they were my trusted friends.

I only offered a snippet of the full story. Yet the few details I shared grabbed their attention. They were mesmerized. Still, I immediately began to second guess myself. Why? Because I saw pain and reservation evident in their facial expressions and body language. I could almost hear them saying to themselves, "That poor guy. Is he alright? How could anyone survive such an ordeal? Is it really possible to survive without a colon? Maybe I should be feeling sorry for him, not learning leadership lessons from him."

As I stood facing that audience, I quickly rethought my position, changed the subject right there on stage and resolved never to mention my ordeal publicly again. It was just too risky. I didn't want their sympathy. I returned to my tried and true material.

At the conclusion of my presentation, a number of people approached me. They offered positive comments regarding my talk. A few mentioned their friends or family members who suffer from Crohn's disease or ulcerative colitis. They thanked me for sharing my personal insights.

For the ten minutes or so that these conversations continued, I noticed one person in particular standing back, away from the others. He seemed to be waiting to speak with me. He looked like a cowboy.

He wasn't really a cowboy. He was a public manager, but his name tag indicated he was from Texas and he sure looked like the strong, silent type. He was more than six feet tall, rugged and rawboned. I guessed him to be in his mid-30's.

As he approached, I smiled and extended my hand. He took it and we shook. His eyes remained securely fixed on mine. He was friendly, but intense. He spoke first.

"I enjoyed your comments," he said seriously.

"Well, thank you," I replied with genuine gratitude.

"I especially appreciated your telling about losing your colon. That must have been a pretty rough time for you."

The emotion I had earlier been able to control, now, for some reason, began to inch toward the surface. *I knew I never should have brought the thing up in the first place*, I fumed to myself. I decided to skirt the issue as best I could.

"It was difficult," I admitted casually. "But that's behind me. I feel great now," I added, hoping to defer further conversation about the subject. He didn't take the hint. Instead, he hit me with a question for which I was totally unprepared.

"Mr. Van Hooser, I'm curious. Do you feel sorry for people who haven't experienced what you did?"

"Excuse me?" I asked, more than a little confused by the question.

"Have you gotten to the point that you feel sorry for folks who haven't gone through what you went through?" he repeated.

What kind of idiotic question is that? I thought. Nevertheless, I tried to remain professional and measured in my response.

"No, honestly, I can't say that I have. In fact, knowing what I've been through, I wouldn't wish that ordeal on my worst enemy."

"Even if they could learn something valuable from it?" he countered.

Without the benefit of another word, this young man knelt down before me. In a matter of seconds, he had unlaced his shoe, removed it and his sock and pulled up his pant leg. There before me was a horribly scarred foot, ankle and lower leg. I didn't know what to say. I just stood speechless.

He patted his leg while looking up at me and said matter-of-factly, "A farming accident. I was a teenager and I got my foot caught in a grain auger. It broke all the bones and pulled my foot totally away from the leg. The only thing that held it together was a few patches of hide and a couple of severely stretched ligaments."

The young man replaced his sock and shoe before standing to face me.

"I almost bled to death," he continued. "They didn't know if they could reattach the foot or not. Obviously, they did, but I was in the hospital for months. I was flat on my back with my foot and leg elevated. After that, it took me several years of healing and therapy to get the mobility back. Now, as you can see, it's almost as good as new again."

It didn't look as good as new. Not by a long shot. But I understood what he was saying. He was long past judging the value of his leg on its appearance. His yardstick was functionality. It was "almost as good as new" because he could use it again.

"That's good to hear," I said. "But I'm sorry you had to go through that."

"I'm not. I've done a lot of thinking about this. I believe with all my heart that it was the best thing that ever happened to me. I actually feel sorry for people who haven't had something like this happen to them."

"Why?" I asked sincerely.

"Because they haven't learned the things you and I have learned. They don't know how strong they really are and they don't know where to find their inner strength. They never really expect to experience any major adversity, so they don't prepare themselves for adversity should it come knocking. They don't know who they should confide in and who they can count on. They don't know what it means to really suffer physically and mentally. As a result, they have little empathy for others around them who are really suffering. Worst of all, they don't know how to accept their circumstances, adjust to them and get on with life."

His words hit their mark. He was absolutely right. Then he dropped the final bombshell.

"Phil, you've got to tell people. You're a speaker—a professional communicator. That's what you're good at. People will listen to you. We did. I did."

I've thought of that young man many times during the writing of this book. He's right. Like him, there were many valuable lessons I learned through my experience—lessons that others might find beneficial even if they didn't share the same exact experience. It is my responsibility to make those lessons available for all who might be interested.

In the United States alone, there are estimated to be between one and two *million* people who currently suffer the ill effects of IBD. Estimates indicate that thirty to thirty-five thousand new cases are diagnosed each year. And that is just within our national borders. Millions more suffer on every continent that make up planet earth. I have felt their pain. Hopefully, this book will shine a bright light on a condition that needs greater attention, while offering encouragement and information for patients.

For every person who suffers from IBD, there are five, ten, fifteen, or more family members, friends, neighbors and co-workers who suffer with them. These individuals find themselves trying to understand what is really happening to their loved ones. They are trying to determine what they can do to help. This is not a condition that sufferers feel comfortable discussing freely and easily. Diarrhea, rectal bleeding and the like don't make for easy tabletop conversation. This is hush-hush stuff. Support group members don't know what to do because they don't understand what is happening "behind the scenes." Hopefully, this book has shown you how you can help.

Finally, there are hundreds of thousands of doctors, nurses and other healthcare professionals around the globe who treat the physical needs of their IBD patients without fully comprehending the emotional and psychological impact the disease inflicts. Patients need their medical care providers to know and to care. Hopefully, this book has offered examples of some who are doing it right.

As I conclude this book, I hope that many lessons and ideas have already leapt from its pages into your mind, heart and actions. I hope you are better prepared to deal with your own struggles and to help others deal with theirs.

I have two final challenges for you. The first is I challenge you to get involved. Get involved with your CCFA state chapter or other local support group. Though I am fully recovered from my battle with ulcerative colitis, I have become an active volunteer with CCFA having spoken at various state and national meetings.

In June, 2003, I along with more than two hundred other interested individuals from around the United States participated in an IBD Advocacy Day on Capitol Hill in Washington, D.C. The event allowed us to meet with our elected Representatives and Senators to share the IBD message face-to-face. Along the way, I met many new friends, young and old, who still fight the IBD battle. They need us in their corner. So find a way to get involved.

The second challenge is this. If you found value in this book, then buy an extra copy as a gift for someone else. In so doing, you will not only be helping that individual, but also a multitude of other IBD sufferers. How? I am committed to donating ten percent of all the profits from this book to the Crohn's & Colitis Foundation of America (CCFA) as they continue their tireless research to find a cure for IBD in our lifetime.

You can make your own contribution to CCFA. Just contact the national office:

Crohn's & Colitis Foundation of America
+1.212.685.3440
www.ccfa.org

If you wish to reach me directly, here is the information.

Phillip Van Hooser, MBA, CSP
+1.270.365.1536
info@ItTakesMoreThanGuts.com
www.ItTakesMoreThanGuts.com
www.vanhooser.com

May God continue to bless you and your efforts on behalf of others.

Just for Understanding...

A Glossary of Important Terms

The following words and terms are common to the discussion of Inflammatory Bowel Disease (IBD). These explanations and definitions are offered in "layperson" language. If a more comprehensive explanation is required, please contact your professional healthcare provider.

Abscesses are localized collections of puss surrounding inflamed tissue.

Absorption is the process of nutrients passing from the intestine into the bloodstream.

Adhesions are caused by the joining of normally unconnected body parts by bands of new fibrous tissue.

Adrenal Corticosteroids: see *steroids*

5-Aminosalicylic Acid (5-ASA) is the active component of sulfasalazine, known generically as mesalamine.

Anal Canal: see *colon*

Anal Sphincter Muscles circle the anus and provide bowel control and continence.

Anastomosis is the joining of two ends of the bowel together.

Anemia is lower than normal amounts of hemoglobin and red blood cells in the blood.

Anesthesia is medication that causes a loss of physical sensation with or without the loss of consciousness.

Anus is the opening at the end of the rectum that allows solid waste to be evacuated from the body.

Anus Muscles: see *anal sphincter muscles*

Appliance collects the waste deposited from an ileostomy. Is commonly referred to as a bag.

Asacol: see *mesalamine*

Ascending Colon: see *colon*

Azathioprine is an immunosuppressive drug sometimes used in the treatment of ulcerative colitis that has not responded to other medications. This drug has been shown to be helpful in reducing or eliminating the dependence on corticosteroids in some patients.

Azulfidine: see *sulfasalazine*

Bag: see *appliance*

Biopsy is a small piece of tissue taken from the body for examination under a microscope. A biopsy is taken from the colon by a special instrument attached to the endoscope during the examination of the rectum or colon. A biopsy is used to confirm the diagnosis of Crohn's disease or ulcerative colitis, or to check periodically for the possibility of cancer.

Bowel Movement is the evacuation of solid waste from the body by way of the anus.

Bowel Preparation is a medication that works to empty the colon of stool and bacteria. See also *GoLYTELY.*

Cecum: see *colon*

Chronic Disease is an illness that occurs at frequent intervals over a long period of time.

Colectomy is the surgical removal of the colon. See also *proctocolectomy*.

Colon is also known as the large intestine. Its main functions are the storage of waste and the absorption of fluid. It is comprised of the cecum, ascending colon, transverse colon, descending colon, sigmoid colon, rectum and anal canal.

Colonoscopy is an examination of the colon by way of a flexible, lighted tube inserted through the anus, into the rectum and beyond. Biopsies may be taken as part of this test to screen for colorectal cancer. Sedatives are usually administered to make this procedure more tolerable.

Colon Preparation: see *bowel preparation* and *GoLYTELY*

Colyte: see *GoLYTELY*

Continence is the ability to defer the need to have a bowel movement.

CORT Enema is a steroid enema.

Cortisone: see *steroids*

Cortisteroids: see *steroids*

Crohn's Disease is an inflammatory bowel disease potentially involving all layers of the bowel wall. It may affect any portion of the gastrointestinal tract including the anus, colon, rectum and small intestine and therefore cannot be totally cured by surgical means.

Cyclosporine: see *immunosuppressive agents*

Defecation: see *bowel movement*

Dehydration is an abnormal depletion of body fluids.

Descending Colon: see *colon*

Diarrhea is characterized by abnormally frequent intestinal evacuations or discharges with the stool often being fluid.

Digestion is the process of breaking down food into its simplest chemical compounds so that it can be absorbed.

Digital Examination involves a physician inserting his/her finger through the anus into the rectum for the purpose of assessing the quality of anal sphincter muscles.

Dipentum: see *mesalamine*

Dressing is a type of sterile covering for an open wound.

Duodenum is the first portion of the small intestine. It connects the stomach to the small intestine.

Endoscope is a flexible, lighted tube that is used to examine the rectum and colon.

Endoscopic Procedures involve inserting a flexible, lighted tube through the anus and into the rectum, allowing a physician to examine the rectum and colon. Also see *colonscopy* and *sigmoidoscopy.*

Enterostomal Therapist (E.T.) is a nurse with experience and special training in the field of colon surgery and intestinal stoma care.

E.T.: see *enterostomal therapist*

Feces: see *stool*

Fistulas are abnormal passages leading from the colon to other organs in the lower abdominal cavity.

Flagyl: see *immunosuppressive agents*

Flare-up is the time when IBD is active and a sufferer feels ill.

Gastroenterology is a branch of medicine concerned with the structure, functions, diseases and pathology of the stomach and intestines.

Gastroenterologist is a physician skilled in the science of gastroenterology.

Gastrointestinal (GI) Tract is essentially the human digestive system including the mouth, the esophagus, the stomach, the small intestine, the colon and the anus.

Genetic describes a disease process that is passed from parent to child. Many diseases require both a proper genetic componant and environmental stress to occur.

Glaucoma is an eye disease marked by increased pressure within the eyeball that can result in eye damage and loss of vision.

GoLYTELY is a bowel preparation (colonic lavage) which works to empty the colon of stool and bacteria. (A colon empty of waste contents lowers the risk of infection and other postoperative complications.)

Hemorrhaging is heavy or uncontrollable bleeding.

IBD: see *inflammatory bowel disease*

Ileoanal Anastomosis is the process of joining the ileum and the anus together. This is done after proctocolectomy surgery.

Ileocecal Valve is the valve that regulates the flow of waste material and gases from the small intestine to the colon.

Ileostomy is where the last part of the small intestine (ileum) is attached to the skin.

Ileum is the last portion of the small intestine that connects to the large intestine.

Immune System is the body's natural defense that fights against disease.

Immunosuppressive Agents are helpful for persons who do not respond to 5-ASA (mesalamine) and steroids, or who have recurrent flare-ups of disease when steroids are tapered. Immunosuppression reduces the body's overly aggressive inflammatory response in several conditions in which the body's own defense mechanism is causing disporportional damage to the tissue, as is seen in inflammatory bowel disease, some forms of arthritis and following organ transplant.

Imuran: see *azathioprine*

Incision is an intentional wound made especially in surgery.

Inflammation is a response to tissue injury that causes redness, swelling and pain.

Inflammatory Bowel Disease (IBD) is an illness characterized by inflammation of the small and large intestines. Ulcerative colitis and Crohn's disease are the two diseases that are known as IBD.

Invasive procedures involve some sort of entry into a living body.

IV (Intravenous) Line allows fluids to be inserted directly into a patient's veins to prevent dehydration and administer necessary medications directly into the bloodstream.

Jejunum is the middle portion of the small intestine.

J-Pouch: see *pelvic reservoir*

Large Intestine: see *colon*

Loop Ileostomy is a procedure which allows waste to be evacuated from the body by bypassing the rectum and anus.

Malnutrition is a condition that occurs when the body does not have enough calories, vitamins and minerals to maintain growth and health.

Medications are medical substances.

Mesalamine (5-Aminosalicyclic Acid or 5-ASA) is a drug intended to inhibit substances in the immune system that cause inflammation. It is very effective and has few side effects.

Metronidazole: see *immunosupressive agents*

6-MP (6-Mercaptopurine): see *immunosuppressive agents*

Mucosa is the lining of the bowel.

Mucosal Ulcerative Colitis: see *ulcerative colitis*

Nasogastric (NG) Tube is passed through the nose and into the stomach of a surgical patient once he/she is asleep in order to empty any stomach contents.

Nausea is stomach distress often marked by an urge to vomit.

Neoral: see *cyclosporine*

Nutrients are small chemical units made up of food that is broken down during the process of digestion.

Occult Blood is microscopic particle of blood that can not be seen by the naked eye.

Olsalazine: see *5-ASA*

Osteoporosis is a condition which is characterized by a decrease in bone mass and density which makes bones more fragile.

Ostomy is an operation that creates an artificial passage for bodily waste elimination.

Patient-Controlled Analgesia (PCA) is a pain management method which allows the patient to self-administer pain medication by way of a small medication-infusion pump. Medication dosage is controlled by a computer contained within the pump.
PCA Pump: see *patient-controlled analgesia*

Pentasa: see *mesalamine*

Pelvic Drain is a tube placed in the pelvis to remove fluids which may collect there after surgery, thus reducing the possibilities of infection.

Pelvic Pouch: see *pelvic reservoir*

Pelvic Reservoir is a pouch constructed from an individual's small intestine, after the removal of the entire colon and rectum, to serve as a "new rectum" for the storage of stool. This procedure is commonly referred to as the J-pouch, S-pouch, W-pouch, ileo-anal reservoir, or ileo-anal pull-through operation.

Post Anesthesia Care Unit (PACU) allows careful observation of patients immediately after surgery, for a period of time during recovery from anesthesia. Family members may be allowed to visit the patient during this period.

Pouchitis is an inflammation in the lining of the ileal pouch which occurs in 10-20% of the patients who have had pouches constructed. It is thought to be due to an over-growth of bacteria in the pouch. It is easily treated by a short course of antibiotics.

Prednisone: see *steroids*

Proctitis is inflammation of the rectum.

Proctocolectomy is the surgical removal of the colon and rectum.

Proctoscopic Examination (Flexible Fiberoptic Sigmoidoscopy) is the examination of the rectum to determine what type of inflammation is involved, to rule out Crohn's disease and to determine if a tumor or cancer is present in the rectum.

Purinethol: see *immunosupressive agents*

Rectal Bleeding is blood coming forth from the rectum.

Rectum is the lowest portion of the colon and is a compliant sac, like a reservoir, which can expand as it fills with stool and then relax when empty.

Relapse: see *flare-up*

Remicade: see *immunosuppressive agents*

Remission is the period when IBD is inactive and the person feels well.

Reservoir is a pouch constructed for the storage of stool.

Rheumatrex: see *methotrexate*

Rowasa: see *mesalamine*

Sandimmune: see *cyclosporine*

Sedation is inducing a relaxed easy physical state especially by the use of sedatives (medications).

Sigmoid Colon: see *colon*

Sigmoidoscopy involves inserting a flexible, lighted tube through the anus, rectum and into the sigmoid, or S-shaped lower part of the colon, for the purpose of diagnosing or monitoring disease. Most physicians prefer not to use sedatives for this procedure.

Spirometry Device is an instrument used to measure the volume and speed of air entering and leaving the lungs.

Steroids are powerful immune suppression drugs, usually used in IBD treatment for active cases of ulcerative colitis and Crohn's disease. They can be quite effective for short-term control of flare-ups, but they do not prevent relapses and have serious long-term effects.

Stoma is the pouch on the outer abdominal skin which collects intestinal waste.

Stool Samples are samples of discharged fecal matter (feces).

Stricture is a closure or obstruction of the intestine caused by scar tissue.

Sulfasalazine is an older, but effective, ASA drug containing sulfa, which acts as an antibiotic and further reduces inflammation. It may not be taken by those with sulfa allergies.

Temporary Loop Ileostomy diverts the stream of stool away from a newly created pouch (pelvic reservoir) and "join-up" (anastomosis) at the anal canal until healing is complete. Normally, a temporary loop ileostomy is closed about three months following the initial surgery, but it is possible to wait six to twelve months without problems.

Transverse Colon: see *colon*

Ulcerated is a break in skin or mucous membrane lining.

Ulcerative Colitis is an inflammatory bowel disease marked by chronic inflammation of the lining (mucosa) of the colon and rectum, but never the small intestine. The only way to cure this disease is by total removal of the colon and rectum (protocolectomy).

Urgency is the need to instantly find a bathroom to evacuate stool.

Urinary Catheter is a tube that is inserted into the bladder and connected to a drainage bag. This allows accurate measurement of urine output and kidney function.

Just Ask Phil…

Straight Answers to Difficult Questions

Human beings are naturally curious. We love to investigate. We love to explore. We love to question. Let's face it, we love to know who, what, when, where, why and how concerning almost any situation we encounter. Yet when someone suffers from a chronic illness, especially one like IBD, the questions become more uncomfortable. Questions about bloody stools, rampant diarrhea and intestinal discharge bags don't make for easy conversation. That is the point of this section.

Throughout my experience with ulcerative colitis I have tried to be available to answer important, but often uncomfortable questions from dozens of people who admit to being ignorant, confused or concerned regarding the reality of living with IBD.

The following questions have been asked of me many times. Inquiring minds want to know. Maybe these questions and my answers will be helpful to you or someone you know and care about.

IBD Symptoms & Prevention

Q: What exactly is IBD?

A: IBD is Inflammatory Bowel Disease. The two conditions that constitute IBD are Crohn's disease and ulcerative colitis.

Q: How common is IBD?

A: It is more common than one might think. An estimated one to two million Americans currently suffer from IBD. Another 30,000 to 35,000 are diagnosed with the condition each year. Almost everyone I speak with either suffers from Crohn's disease or ulcerative colitis *or* knows a friend, family member or associate who does.

Q: What are the most common symptoms of IBD?

A: Initial symptoms may be mild or severe and may include persistent diarrhea, pain in the abdomen, fever and noticeable blood in bowel movements. Any of these symptoms are worthy of a visit to your local physician.

Q: Will these symptoms worsen as time goes by?

A: They certainly can. But keep in mind that everyone is different. Some individuals suffer from IBD for a prolonged period of time before they become ill enough to be diagnosed. Others are struck with a severe episode that requires immediate attention. It is always best to get professional medical advice whenever a physical problem is identified.

Q: Can this disease be prevented?

A: At the present time, unfortunately no. Until the specific cause of the disease is isolated and identified there are no known steps that can be taken to avoid it.

The Surgery

Q: Your experience with IBD and ulcerative colitis culminated with surgery to have your colon removed. Was your case the exception or the norm?

A: I was the exception. It is estimated that less than 25% of all those who suffer from ulcerative colitis will ever require surgery to remove their colons. In fact, most patients respond very well to available medications that have been developed to curb the effects of IBD-related diseases. In my case, I was one of the unfortunate minority.

Q: During the removal of your colon, the creation of your J-pouch and the eventual reconnection did you experience any major surgical complications?

A: The short answer is no. However, after the first surgery I was determined to be anemic and I required two units of blood. I also experienced a urinary tract infection related to the urinary catheter that had been used during surgery. Both of these "complications" are rather common following major surgery and were therefore dealt with quickly and successfully. I should stress though that the procedure I underwent is *major surgery* and should never be taken lightly.

Q: After the surgeries did you experience any problem with incontinence?

A: No, I didn't. It's my understanding that episodes of incontinence are normally due to deteriorating or damaged anal sphincter muscles. Neither were problems in my case.

Q: Did the surgeries affect your ability to urinate? Obviously, the emphasis of the surgery was on the intestinal tract, but were there any unforeseen effects on the urinary tract?

A: I experienced no such problems.

Q: Your ileostomy was reversed. Is that always possible or do some people have to wear a bag permanently?

A: The reversal surgery has become very successful in recent years, thereby reducing the number of individuals who must wear a permanent bag. However, various conditions mandate a permanent appliance over a temporary one. Your physician will be able to offer more detail.

Q: How big are your scars? Will they eventually fade away?

A: My abdominal scar is approximately ten to eleven inches in length and runs north and south—from just below my breast bone to my pelvic region. My stoma scar is oval-shaped, about the size of an egg, and is on my lower right abdomen. The scars are now about three years old and both have "faded" and softened significantly. However, both are still noticeable and I suspect they always will be.

Living with A Bag

Q: How difficult was it to adjust to the bag once the surgery was complete?

A: Honestly, the physical adjustment was much easier than the psychological adjustment. I have discovered that the fear of the unknown is often worse than the reality of our individual experiences. I worried quite a bit about life with the bag before the surgery. However, once the bag was my new reality, I changed my attitude and adjusted very quickly. For most people, myself included, the *idea* of wearing a bag is worse than the *reality* of wearing one.

Q: How large was the bag?

A: I have described it as being approximately the size of a small bag of popcorn. Slightly wider and somewhat shorter. The bag was attached to the opening in my right side just below my waist line.

Q: Was it difficult to dispose of the contents of the bag?

A: Not at all. It involved the simple act of sitting on a commode, locating the bottom of the bag between my legs, releasing the clip on the bottom of the bag and allowing the bag's contents to empty into the toilet bowl. Once the bag was empty, the bottom could be wiped clean with toilet tissue and the clip replaced securing the bottom of the bag. The entire process took between two and four minutes.

Q: How often did the bag need to be changed? Was it difficult to do so?

A: Temporary bags like mine needed to be changed every three or four days. It is my understanding that folks who wear a permanent ileostomy or colostomy need to change there appliances about once a week. The technology is constantly improving. As for changing the bag, there is a process that needs to be followed which requires thorough cleaning of the site (with soap and water) and proper preparation of the skin to ensure a secure seal for the appliance. But the procedure is simple and took about ten to fifteen minutes to complete.

Q: I understand the bag is designed to capture both waste and gas exiting the intestines. Did you experience problems with odors or unpleasant sounds? If so, how did you manage these?

A: Neither of these issues was a major problem for me. There was some odor, but just when the bag was emptied. In other words, it was no worse than the odor associated with a "normal" bowel movement. I think the appliances themselves have been improved significantly over the years to deal with the odor issue.

As for sounds, well, they do happen. Can they be a bit embarrassing? Sure. But I chose to look at the positive side. First, I was healthy and that was most important. I wasn't about to let a little side effect diminish the focus on my improved health. Second, for those people who knew about my condition, there was absolutely no problem. They understood. For those individuals who didn't know about my condition, it offered me an opportunity to both inform and educate them as to how hundreds of thousands of individuals live their lives.

Q: What physical limitations did wearing a bag impose upon you?

A: Almost none. I exercised, worked, walked and ran while wearing a bag. I did learn to sleep on my back instead of my stomach because it was more comfortable to do so. I didn't try swimming or standing on my head, though I know both would have been possible. The two things a wearer wants to avoid is a severe physical blow to the lower abdominal area and anything that would cause the bag to spring a leak. Wearers are wise to carry a spare appliance with them should an unexpected accident occur.

Q: What impact did wearing a bag have on your relationships with family and friends?

A: To a person, my family and friends were curious and interested in learning more about my health, the surgeries I endured and of course, the bag. Some just wanted an explanation while others wanted to see the actual bag for themselves. Depending on the appropriateness of the situation I tried to accommodate them as best I could. I saw (and still see) this as an opportunity to help many people broaden their personal understanding of a condition that often stays intentionally hidden.

Q: Do you think others in a similar condition are wise to be as open as you were?

A: It all depends on the individual. If he or she chooses to share as I did, I expect he or she will experience the same level of personal satisfaction I did. I saw my role as one of offering others education. However, if they choose not to do so, they should not feel as if they are under any sort of obligation.

Diet

Q: How has your diet changed from the point of being diagnosed with IBD until now?

A: Immediately after the original diagnosis my doctor had me try various diets to see if one of them would help reduce the severity of my flare-ups. I tried high fiber and low fiber diets. I eliminated all dairy products and red meat from my diet for a time. I stopped eating foods with nuts, seeds and shells. The only food I tolerated well was turkey sandwiches on wheat bread.

Today, almost three years after the initial surgery my diet has become more predictable. For the most part, I can eat whatever I want. But there are a few foods that I have learned will cause me digestive distress. I consciously avoid most spicy foods, foods that are extremely greasy, chocolate and carbonated beverages.

Q: How was your weight affected throughout the process?

A: At the onset of my bout with IBD, I weighed 202 pounds (about 15 to 20 pounds more than my 5'9" frame should have been carrying). As the flare-ups intensified I started losing significant amounts of weight. In total I lost almost fifty pounds. Today, three years after the surgeries, my weight is holding steady at about 185 pounds.

Q: Do you get gas more or less frequently as compared to before your surgery?

A: Without question I get gas less frequently than before surgery. That may be a function of my new diet or a by-product of losing my diseased colon—or a combination of both.

Q: What foods do you miss most?

A: Without question that would be Mr. Goodbar candy bars, chocolate chip cookies and fudge brownies. But I don't miss them enough to wish things were the way they were before.

Q: Can you drink alcohol after having your colon removed?

A: I am not a drinker so I can't answer this question from first-hand experience. I suggest you consult your physician for advice.

Medications

Q: What kind of medications did you take in the early stages of your battle with IBD?

A: The two primary medications I took were first Pentasa and later Asacol. Both are wonderful drugs that help many IBD sufferers control their symptoms and keep their disease in remission. Unfortunately, neither of the drugs was successful in curbing my flare-ups. The only drug that worked well for me was Prednisone, a steroid. Because of the long-term ill-effects of this medication, I eventually opted for the surgical removal of my colon.

Q: Are you taking any kinds of medication for your condition now?

A: I am not taking any prescription medication at all. I haven't since I left the hospital more than two and a half years ago. However, I do take a number of vitamins and nutritional supplements each day. Specifically, I take a multi-vitamin, Vitamin C, Vitamin E and Omega 3 Fish Oil tablets. In case of an emergency, my doctor has provided me a standing prescription for Immodium. To this point, I have never had to have it filled.

After the Fact

Q: Now that you are through the surgeries, how have your bathroom habits changed? How often do you have to go?

A: The removal of my colon and rectum, despite the construction of the J-pouch, significantly reduced the storage capacity for my fecal waste. Therefore, where I might have had one bowel movement a day when my colon was healthy, I now have six to eight bowel movements per day now that my colon is gone. The actual number varies depending on what—and how much—I eat and drink. On the bright side, the six to eight bathroom trips are significantly better than the 15 to 25 trips I was averaging during flare-ups while I still possessed my diseased colon. On top of that, I now have up to an hour or longer to find a bathroom when it is time to go, versus minutes before.

Q: Today are your bowel movements painful or uncomfortable in any way?

A: For the most part there is no pain or discomfort associated with my bowel movements. The one exception is if I eat foods that are excessively spicy, those foods tend to burn going in *and* coming out. I keep a tube of Johnson & Johnson's Prevacare ointment on hand to help control the burning and itching.

Q: Is your quality of life better now than before the surgeries?

A: Absolutely. There is simply no comparison. Knowing what I know now, I would do it all again without a moment's hesitation.

Q: What if any physical restrictions do you currently have as you function without a colon?

A: There are no significant restrictions that I am aware of. My physical strength is not quite at the same level it was prior to my bout with IBD and the surgeries that followed, but advancing age may also be a contributing factor in that equation. The only restriction that I remain conscious of is the enhanced possibility of dehydration. Since my colon is no longer available to absorb liquids and re-hydrate my body, I consciously consume considerably more liquids, specifically more water than I did before.

Q: How does this type of surgery affect sexual intimacy?

A: It is my understanding that less than 10% of the people experiencing the surgical procedure detailed in this book end up suffering from some sort of sexual dysfunction. I experienced no such problems. Before my surgeries my sexual desire was severely limited due primarily to my failing health. As soon as my body had healed sufficiently from the first surgery, while wearing the ileostomy, sexual relations resumed. Soon after the second (reversal) surgery sexual intimacy was back to normal. I see no reason why a couple's love life should be negatively affected by this type of surgery if the relationship is built on a foundation of unqualified love and mutual respect. Love will find a way.

Q: Is there any reason to believe that the type of surgery you experienced will shorten your anticipated life span?

A: I have found no reason to believe that might be the case. And I do know the quality of life is better than it was.

Q: Did this experience shake your faith in God?

A: No. I never wondered why I was having to go through the experience. I never entertained the thought that God had somehow forsaken me. All I needed to do was look around and see others fighting more difficult battles than mine—day after day after day—to know that I was still blessed. Blessed by living in a land that provided quality health care for conditions such as mine. Blessed by having friends and family to support me. Blessed by being able to learn so much through the experience. That was the motivation for this book. I now wish to share what I learned with others.

Q: I don't have a strong support system like yours. What suggestions do you have for getting though such a challenging ordeal?

A: My advice would be to contact the Crohn's & Colitis Foundation of America. They will be able to put you in touch with the CCFA chapter nearest you. There you will find caring, understanding individuals to share with and learn from.

Another source would be hospitals. Most major hospitals that perform colorectal surgery have patient support groups that you could become a part of. For those who are comfortable using a computer, on-line chat rooms might be an option.

Finally, I suggest you might also find great benefit by affiliating with a church or synagogue where you live. A community of faith can offer tremendous encouragement during periods of need.

I hope these questions and answers have been helpful to you. If there are other questions you would like to see addressed, please e-mail them to **questions@ItTakesMoreThanGuts.com**.

Just the Facts...
About IBD

Are you in hurry to gather information? You don't have time to read *It Takes More Than Guts* from cover to cover? Maybe you prefer what I call the *Joe Friday approach.* Who is Joe Friday? Trivia buffs know that Joe Friday was the police detective on the 1960's *Dragnet* television series. Sgt. Friday was not a fan of small talk. He preferred to cut to the heart of a matter with his signature line, "The facts, ma'am. Just the facts."

Well, here are the facts about Inflammatory Bowel Disease. Note, the ***bold, italicized*** words are defined in the **Glossary** section of this book.

What is the Gastrointestinal (GI) Tract?

The ***gastrointestinal (GI) tract*** is essentially the human digestive system. It extends from the mouth to the anus, including the esophagus, the stomach, the small intestine and the ***colon*** (large intestine).

Food travels into the mouth, through the esophagus and into the stomach where it is broken down into particles small enough to pass through into the small intestine. The small intestine is approximately 20 feet long and consists of three sections: the ***duodenum***, the ***jejunum*** and finally the ***ileum***. Most of the nutrients from food are absorbed into the lining of the small intestine and distributed throughout the body by way of the blood stream.

The liquid waste residue that remains once the nutrients have been absorbed passes from the ileum into the colon. This waste material slowly makes its way through the various portions of the approximately six foot colon, from the ***cecum***, up through the ***ascending colon*** (upper right quadrant), across the abdomen through the ***transverse colon*** (upper left quadrant) and then down the ***descending*** and ***sigmoid colon*** to the ***rectum***.

During this process, the liquid from the waste is absorbed into the lining of the colon and is used to re-hydrate the body. The solid waste or feces which remains is stored in the rectum until it is convenient to discharge it completely from the body by way of the anus.

What is Inflammatory Bowel Disease (IBD)?

Inflammatory Bowel Disease (IBD) is a general term which includes ***ulcerative colitis*** and ***Crohn's disease***. These ***chronic*** gastrointestinal disorders are brought about by unknown causes.

Ulcerative colitis is an inflammatory disease restricted to the colon. Ulcers form in the inner lining, or ***mucosa***, of the colon or rectum.

Crohn's Disease is an inflammation that extends into the deeper layers of the intestinal wall. This disorder can develop in any part of the gastrointestinal tract, though it is most often found in the ileum and the first part of the large intestine (cecum).

What Causes IBD?

Unfortunately, the actual cause of IBD remains mystery. Until a specific cause is determined, a cure cannot be found. Fortunately, by way of research, some things are becoming clearer.

Genetic Factors

- Up to 25% of IBD sufferers have family members with the disease.
- Recent studies seem to indicate genetic abnormalities or both ulcerative colitis and Crohn's disease may share locations on chromosones 3, 7 and 12.

Immune System

- Some researchers believe that the disease develops because something (i.e., genetic susceptibility, virus or bacteria) triggers an abnormal, over reactive immune response.

- When intestinal inflammation occurs, the immune system seems to release white blood cells which produce damaging proteins. These proteins produce additional intestinal inflammation and damage which attracts more white blood cells.
- Thus, a vicious, destructive loop is created.

Diet

- IBD is more prevalent in industrialized countries, therefore, some experts believe environmental factors, such as diet may play some role.
- Unfortunately, various diet studies can be conflicting, confusing and unreliable.

What are the Symptoms of IBD?

Ulcerative colitis and Crohn's disease share many symptoms. Both are ***chronic diseases***. Symptoms can alternately ***flare-up*** and then revert to periods of ***remission***, leaving sufferers symptom free.

Symptoms can be barely noticeable, mild, severe and even disabling. They can develop gradually or strike suddenly. Specific symptoms may include:

- Persistent diarrhea
- Constipation
- Abdominal pain or cramps
- Blood passing through the rectum
- Fever
- Weight loss
- Joint, skin or eye irritations
- Delayed growth and retarded sexual maturation in children

Ulcerative colitis is considered *mild* if a patient exhibits the following symptoms:

- 4 or less bowel movements a day

- Only occasional blood in the ***stool***
- A normal temperature, pulse rate and red blood cell count
- And no abnormalities observed on x-rays of the colon

Ulcerative colitis is considered *serious* if the following symptoms are present:

- More than 6 bowel movements a day
- Frequent to persistent blood in the stool
- Fever
- A rapid pulse
- Anemia
- Abnormal x-rays of the colon
- Tenderness in the abdomen when pressed

Crohn's disease is considered *mild* when:

- There are few bowel movements.
- Abdominal pain is absent or minimal.
- The patient has an overall sense of well being that is normal or close to normal.

Crohn's disease is considered *severe* when:

- Frequent bowel movements require anti-diarrhea medication.
- Abdominal pain is severe (pain is normally felt in the lower right quadrant of the abdomen).
- Red blood cell count is low.
- The patient has a poor sense of well being and experiences such as weight loss, joint pain, inflammation in the eyes, reddened or ulcerated skin, ***fistulas***, ***abscesses*** and fever.

Who Gets IBD?

- An estimated one to two million Americans suffer from IBD, with there being a roughly equal incidence of ulcerative colitis and Crohn's disease.
- Each year, approximately 30,000 new cases are diagnosed.
- Males and females are equally susceptible.

- IBD is diagnosed most often between the ages of 15 and 40.
- A lesser peak onset period occurs between 50 and 80 years of age.
- About 2% of IBD cases appear in children below the age of 10.
- 30% occur in young people between the ages of 10 and 19.
- Jewish people of European descent have a risk of IBD 5 times that of the general population.
- The condition occurs more frequently in the United States, Western Europe, Canada, New Zealand and Australia than in other parts of the world.
- IBD appears to be more common among city than country dwellers.

How is IBD Diagnosed?

It is important to see a physician and get a thorough examination when IBD symptoms are identified. IBD may be diagnosed by the following:

- An elevated number of white blood cells may indicate the presence of inflammation.
- ***Stool samples*** that indicate blood or infections.
  In children, noticeable slowed growth.
- ***Endoscopic procedures***.

How Serious Is IBD?

Besides the personal suffering experienced during flare-ups, the long-term implications of IBD are worthy of note. Some of the conditions to be aware of include:

- *Fistulas*. Deep ulcers in Crohn's disease frequently result in the development of fistulas, channels that burrow between organs, loops of the intestine, or between the intestine and the skin. They often form pockets of infection or abscesses, which may become life threatening without treatment. Fistulas are rare in ulcerative colitis.

- *Intestinal blockage*. Inflammation from Crohn's disease can produce patches of scar tissue known as ***strictures***. These can eventually constrict the passages of the intestines, causing bowel obstruction with severe cramps and vomiting.

- *Cancer.* Chronic ulcerative colitis increases the risk for colon cancer. In different studies, the risk has been estimated to be 5-10% after 10 years and 15-40% after 30 years. Patients with Crohn's disease of the colon have a similar risk for colon cancer.
- *Emotional factors.* IBD is not a psychosomatic illness, yet the potential emotional consequences of IBD are significant. Missed school and lost work time due to flare-ups can have a negative emotional effect. Over time, sufferers may begin to associate eating with the fear of abdominal pain. Frequent attacks of diarrhea can cause a strong sense of humiliation, resulting in low self-esteem and social isolation.

What Kind of Diets Work for IBD?

Many medical professionals promote the adoption of a low fiber diet for their Crohn's and ulcerative colitis patients. Low fiber diets are intended to control the intake of fiber and therefore limit fecal output by restricting foods high in crude fiber, cellulose, hemicellulose and lignin. Foods that increase fecal residue such as milk and milk products are also restricted. This diet recommends that total dietary fiber per day should not exceed 15-20 grams (4 grams crude fiber).

A sampling of foods to include and foods to avoid in a Low Fiber Diet would include:

Food Groups	Daily Servings	Foods to Include	Foods to Avoid
Milk	2 cups (if tolerated)	Skim, buttermilk, low fat, plain yogurt	More than two cups used as a beverage, chocolate milk, cocoa
Meat, Fish, Poultry, Cheese, Meat alternatives	4-5 oz.	Lean beef, chicken, lamb, liver, turkey, pork, ham (if tolerated); smooth peanut butter; fresh fish,	Fried, cured, salty or processed meats, such as cold cuts, hot dogs; crunchy peanut butter; strong cheeses, such as cheddar or

		salmon; cottage cheese, American or mild-flavored cheese	limburger; sausage; dried beans and peas
Egg	1 per day	Any style except fried	Fried, raw eggs
Bread and cereal	4 or more servings	Enriched bread made with finely milled whole grain or refined flour; cooked and dry refined cereals such as plain instant oatmeal, puffed rice, Rice Krispies, Corn Flakes; saltine crackers	Breads made with seeds, coarse whole meal and cracked wheat breads; coarse cereal such as shredded wheat, old-fashioned oatmeal; whole grain crackers
Potato and alternate	1-2 1/2 cup servings	White or sweet potato (without skin or frying); rice, spaghetti, noodles, macaroni, pasta	Potato skins, fried potatoes, potato chips
Vegetable	2 or more 1/2 cup servings	Tender, cooked vegetables; strained pureed corn; tomato juice	Raw vegetables, vegetables with skins, whole kernel corn
Fat	3 or more servings	Margarine, oils, butter, cream, shortening, sour cream, mayonnaise, cream cheese	Avocado; all other fats
Fruit	2 or more 1/2 cup servings	Fruit juice, citrus fruit sections without membrane, stewed or canned fruit without seeds	All raw fruit; spiced, pickled or dried fruits; pineapple, berries, prune juice
Sweets & Desserts	As desired	Hard candy, gumdrops, jelly beans, clear jelly,	Those made with nuts, coconut, seeds, jams with

		honey, syrup, cakes, cookies, puddings, ice cream (plain) using allowed milk	seeds and skins; desserts containing chocolate
Beverage	As desired	Tea, coffee, decaffeinated coffee, carbonated beverages, fruit beverages	Alcohol, milk or milk drinks in excess of 2 cups per day
Soup	As desired	Broth, bouillon, noodle or rice soups with meat, cream soups (using allowed milk)	Highly seasoned soup
Miscellaneous	As desired	Salt and mild seasonings	Pepper, chili powder, barbeque spice, garlic, vinegar, steak sauce, any other strongly flavored spice or herb

What Drug Treatments Are Available for IBD?

Drugs cannot cure IBD, but they are effective in reducing the inflammation and accompanying symptoms in up to 80% of patients. The primary goal of drug therapy is to reduce inflammation in the intestines. The success of drug therapy is determined by its ability to induce and maintain ***remissions*** without incurring significant side effects. Specific catagories of drugs include:

Mesalamine (5-Aminosalicylic Acid or ***5-ASA)***

This drug is intended to inhibit substances in the immune system that cause inflammation. Mesalamine is very effective and has few side effects. Unfortunately, it is quickly absorbed into the upper gastrointestinal tract before it reaches the colon.

In recent years, new 5-ASA preparations have received Federal Drug Administration (FDA) approval for ulcerative colitis. ***Asacol***, ***Rowasa***, ***Dipentum*** and ***Pentasa*** have been developed with special coatings which allow the medications to make their way through the length of the gastrointestinal tract and into the colon before the medication is released. Though they have not been approved for this application, Asacol and Pentasa are useful in treating Crohn's disease because they are delivered to the small intestine.

Adrenal Corticosteroids *(***Steroids***)*

Steroids are powerful anti-inflammatory drugs, usually used only for *active* ulcerative colitis and Crohn's disease. They can be quite effective for short-term control of acute flare-ups. However, they do not prevent relapses and have serious long-term effects, so they are not recommended for maintenance therapy.

Prednisone is the most commonly used steroid. A major problem with steroids is that they cannot be restricted to only local areas of the intestines. In fact, they circulate throughout the body, which can cause wide spread side effects. Potential long-term side effects are many and can include: susceptibility to infection, weight gain and puffiness, acne, excess hair growth, hypertension, accelerated osteoporosis, cataracts, glaucoma, diabetes, wasting of the muscles and menstrual irregularities. Personality changes can also occur, including irritability, insomnia, psychosis and depression. Growth may be retarded in children.

Immunomodulatory Medicines *or* **Immunosuppressive Agents**

Continuing research supports the theory that IBD is directly affected by the role of an over active immune system. Currently, immunosuppressive agents such as ***azathioprine*** (***Imuran***) and ***6-mercaptopurine*** (***6-MP***, ***Purinethol***) are proving helpful to in persons who do not respond to 5-ASA and steroids, or who have recurrent flare-ups of disease when steroids are tapered. Other drugs are used on occasion. ***Metronidazole*** (***Flagyl***) is useful in Crohn's disease. ***Clyclosporine*** is useful in acutely severe ulcerative colitis situations. ***Nicotine*** can also be helpful.

New treatments are constantly in development. One of these, ***Remicade***, has been approved by the FDA for treatment of patients with moderate to severe Crohn's disease who have not responded to conventional therapy.

What Role Does Surgery Play In IBD?

Surgery sometimes becomes necessary when medications can no longer control the physical effects of IBD, when there are intestinal obstructions, or when other complications arise.

An estimated two-thirds to three-quarters of persons with Crohn's disease will have one or more operations in the course of their lifetime. However, the surgery for Crohn's is not considered a permanent cure, since the disease usually recurs.

For ulcerative colitis, surgical removal of the entire colon and rectum (***procotocolectomy***) is a permanent cure. Approximately 20-30% of ulcerative colitis patients will eventually experience such a procedure. In most cases today, the function of the ***anal sphincter*** muscles can be preserved with a ***ileoanal pouch*** procedure and a permanent ***colostomy*** can be avoided.

Sources

Crohn's & Colitis Foundation of America (CCFA)

drkoop.com
Medical Encyclopedia
diagnosishealth.com

Medical Clinics of North America **(1979)**

Nutrition and Diet Therapy **(1979)**

Mayo Clinic Diet Manual: A Handbook of Dietary Practices **(1981)**

W.A. Shands Teaching Hospital and Clinics: Guide to Normal Nutrition and Diet Modification Manual **(1977)**

Clinical Nutrition **(1980)**

Diet Manual: Utilizing A Vegetarian Diet Plan **(1978)**

Handbook of Clinical Dietetics: American Dietetic Association **(1981)**

It Takes More Than Guts

To Survive Chronic Illness

Phillip Van Hooser provides these additional resources to help patients, support groups, medical professionals, companies and associations understand the human side of coping with chronic illness.

1. **Read...*It Takes More Than Guts.***

   This book will give the patient, caregiver and medical staff a firsthand view of living with and surviving IBD. Discounts are available for volume purchases. Contact us for specific quotes.

2. **Watch...*It Takes More Than Guts...Caring in Action.***

   Through interviews with family members, friends and gastroenterology specialists, this powerful DVD tells the story of supporting and caring for a chronically ill loved one. Available in DVD format only. Discounts are available for volume purchases. Contact us for specific quotes.

3. **Invite...Phillip Van Hooser to speak to your employees or at your upcoming association meeting or medical conference.**

   As both an award winning professional speaker *and* IBD survivor, Phillip Van Hooser delivers powerful and inspiring keynote addresses that are certain to resonate with your audience. Healthcare organizations that are in the business of treating supporting IBD and other chronically ill patients will value Phil's firsthand experience and practical insight.

For more information on Phillip Van Hooser's availability and fees, or to order *It Takes More Than Guts* books and DVDs, contact us at:

www.ItTakesMoreThanGuts.com

or

+1.270.365.1536